NATIONAL CENTER FOR EDUCATION STATISTICS

THE 1990 SCIENCE REPORT CARD

NAEP'S Assessment of Fourth, Eighth, and Twelfth Graders

Lee R. Jones • Ina V.S. Mullis • Senta A. Raizen
Iris R. Weiss • Elizabeth A. Weston

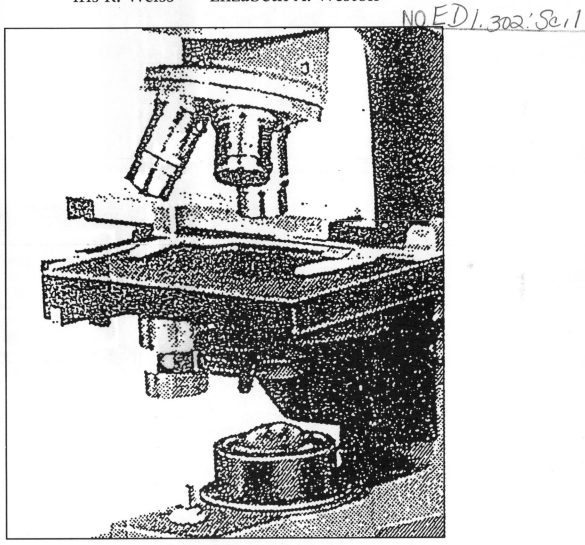

March 1992

THE NATION'S REPORT CARD naep

Prepared by EDUCATIONAL TESTING SERVICE under contract
with the National Center for Education Statistics

Office of Educational Research and Improvement
U.S. Department of Education

U.S. Department of Education
Lamar Alexander
Secretary

Office of Educational Research and Improvem
Diane Ravitch
Assistant Secretary and Counselor to the Secretar

National Center for Education Statistics
Emerson J. Elliott
Acting Commissioner

FOR MORE INFORMATION

For ordering information on this report, write:

Education Information Branch
Office of Educational Research and Improvement
U.S. Department of Education
555 New Jersey Avenue, NW
Washington, D.C. 20208-5641

or call 1-800-424-1616 (in the Washington, D.C. metropolitan area call 202-219-1651).

Library of Congress, Catalog Card Number: 92-60173

ISBN: 0-88685-124-6

The work upon which this publication is based was performed for the National Center for Education Statistics, Office of Educational Research and Improvement, by Educational Testing Service.

Educational Testing Service is an equal opportunity/affirmative action employer.

Educational Testing Service, ETS, and (ETS) are registered trademarks of Educational Testing Service.

TABLE OF CONTENTS

V

OVERVIEW

*I*n September 1989, at the National Education Summit in Charlottesville, Virginia, President Bush and the nation's governors adopted six ambitious national education goals.[1] The President listed these six goals at the presentation of the national education strategy in April 1991:

First, ensure that every child starts school ready to learn; second, raise the high school graduation rate to 90 percent; third, ensure that each American student leaving the fourth, eighth, and twelfth grades can demonstrate competence in core subjects; fourth, make our students first in the world in math and science achievement; fifth, ensure that every American adult is literate and has the skills necessary to compete in a global economy and exercise the rights and responsibilities of citizenship; and sixth, liberate every American school from drugs and violence so that schools encourage learning.[2]

The science achievement results presented in this report pertain directly to three of these national goals. First, the report presents findings for fourth, eighth, and twelfth graders in the core subject of science and second, it provides a national context for considering students' strengths and weaknesses in science and contemplating how these compare with students' skills in other industrialized nations. Perhaps less obviously, but even more importantly, the science achievement results have a direct bearing on the fifth goal. Science education helps prepare individuals to be informed and active participants in civic life, productive workers, and lifelong learners. Maintaining a strong participatory democracy, strengthening our nation's economy, and continuing to achieve advancements in science and technology all demand a scientifically literate citizenry.

---

[1] *Educating America: State Strategies for Achieving the National Education Goals* (Washington, D.C.: National Governors' Association, 1991).

[2] *AMERICA 2000: An Education Strategy* (Washington, D.C.: U.S. Department of Education, 1991).

National attention to the quality of science education is further highlighted by a series of reports urging improvements in the science knowledge and skills of our nation's students as they prepare to compete in a world that is becoming more and more technologically sophisticated.[3] Scientific research has yielded rich dividends of knowledge and, through technology, produced solutions to innumerable practical problems. Further, solid scientific understanding is vital for all citizens in our contemporary culture where science and technology permeate daily life. Yet, a number of studies released during the past decade have documented the inadequate knowledge and performance of U.S. students in science.[4] In particular, the results described in this report support those presented for NAEP's long-term trend assessment in science in the recent report *Trends in Academic Progress: Achievement of U.S. Students in Science, 1969-70 to 1990; Mathematics, 1973 to 1990; Reading, 1971 to 1990; and Writing, 1984 to 1990.*[5]

This report from The Nation's Report Card provides further information about students' lack of preparation in science, their apparent disinclination to enroll in challenging science courses, and the comparatively low achievement of Black and Hispanic students, females, economically disadvantaged students, and non-college bound students. These Science Report Card results are based on a national survey of nearly 20,000 students in grades 4, 8, and 12, conducted during the winter and spring of 1990 by the National Assessment of Educational Progress (NAEP). Each student participating in the assessment answered a series of constructed-response and multiple-choice questions designed to measure his or her knowledge and understanding of the life sciences, the physical sciences, the earth and space sciences, and the nature of science. Information about their science experiences and instruction was collected from students at all three grades, and the teachers of eighth graders who participated in the assessment also completed questionnaires about their background, training, and instructional approaches. Because of the

---

[3] *Science for All Americans: A Project 2061 Report on Literacy Goals in Science, Mathematics, and Technology* (Washington, D.C.: American Association for the Advancement of Science, 1989).

Fulfilling the Promise: Biology Education in the Nation's Schools (Washington, D.C.: National Research Council, Committee on High School Biology Education, 1991).

Criteria for Excellence (Washington, D.C.: National Science Teachers Association, 1987).

[4] *Educating Americans for the 21st Century: A Report to the American People and the National Science Board* (Washington, D.C.: National Science Board Commission on Precollege Education in Mathematics, Science, and Technology, 1983).

A Nation at Risk: The Imperative for Educational Reform (Washington, D.C.: Office of Technology Assessment, 1988).

Ina V.S. Mullis and Lynn B. Jenkins, *The Science Report Card: Elements of Risk and Recovery* (Princeton, NJ: National Assessment of Educational Progress, Educational Testing Service, 1988).

[5] Ina V.S. Mullis et. al., *Trends in Academic Progress: Achievement of U.S. Students in Science, 1969-70 to 1990; Mathematics, 1973 to 1990; Reading, 1971 to 1990; and Writing, 1984 to 1990* (Washington, D.C.: U.S. Department of Education, 1991).

relatively low amount of science instruction at grade 4, and the large percentage of high-school seniors not enrolled in science courses, eighth grade was judged as the best among the three grades for collecting teacher information. Additionally, the middle school years are often students' first major encounter with science, and therefore can be particularly influential in laying the groundwork for future science study.

The results from the 1990 science assessment were analyzed using item response theory (IRT) methods, allowing NAEP to describe performance across the grades and subpopulations on a 0 to 500 proficiency scale. Along this continuum, four levels of proficiency were defined:

Level 200: Understands Simple Scientific Principles

Level 250: Applies General Scientific Information

Level 300: Analyzes Scientific Procedures and Data

Level 350: Integrates Specialized Scientific Information

Descriptions of the knowledge, skills, and understandings represented at each level were developed based on the types of questions answered correctly by the students performing at each level. (More detailed information on the 1990 NAEP science assessment and the proficiency scale can be found throughout this report and in Appendices A and B.)

HIGHLIGHTS FROM NAEP'S
1990 SCIENCE REPORT CARD

● Fewer than one-half of the nation's high-school seniors demonstrated the knowledge and reasoning abilities typical of performance at Level 300, which included applying scientific knowledge to interpret data in tables and graphs, evaluating and designing science experiments, and possessing some in-depth knowledge of scientific information.

● Approximately two-thirds of the nation's eighth graders and approximately one-third of the fourth graders demonstrated the knowledge typical of performance at Level 250, which included understanding basic information in the physical sciences and basic ecological principles, and a beginning ability to interpret experimental results.

● At grades 4, 8, and 12, large disparities in science proficiency existed between White and Asian/Pacific Islander students and their Black and Hispanic counterparts. These differences occurred in each of the four content areas covered by the NAEP science assessment — the life sciences, physical sciences, earth and space sciences, and the nature of science.

• No gender difference in overall science proficiency existed at grade 4. However, there were statistically significant differences favoring males at both grades 8 and 12. The number of content areas in which males held an achievement advantage increased with each grade assessed. At grade 4, males had higher proficiency than females only in the earth and space sciences, but at grade 8 they also had higher proficiency in physical science. At grade 12, males had higher average proficiency than females in all three traditional science disciplines. In contrast, at all three grades, females had higher proficiency than did males in the nature of science.

• Socioeconomic status also was related to student achievement in science. At all three grades, students from advantaged urban communities performed better than students from disadvantaged urban communities. Also, average science achievement showed a positive relationship with parents' education level.

• NAEP's results by region revealed that fourth, eighth, and twelfth graders from the Northeast had higher average proficiency than their grade-level counterparts from the Southeast. High school seniors from the Southeast had lower science achievement, on average, than those from each of the other three regions of the country.

• Several factors in the students' home environment also were related to proficiency in science. At all three grades, students who had access to more reading materials in the home performed better, on average, than students who had access to fewer materials; students who watched six or more hours of television each day had lower average proficiency than those who watched less television; and students who had both parents living at home had higher average proficiency than those from single parent families or those who lived apart from both parents.

• Among high school seniors, average science proficiency increased progressively in direct relation to the number of science courses taken. Most students reported taking at least a year of coursework in biology, but only about half reported taking a year or more of chemistry, and even fewer — 29 percent — reported taking physics courses for that length of time. Similar percentages of males and females had taken a year or more of both biology and chemistry, but a higher percentage of males than females had taken that much physics.

• Schools do not place a special priority on science, particularly at the fourth-grade level. Fewer than half of the fourth graders attended elementary schools that placed a special priority on science, and fewer than one-third of twelfth graders attended high schools that did so. In addition, only half of the fourth graders reported having instruction in science almost every day.

● Most students reported that they liked science, but the percentages of students so reporting was lower at grades 8 and 12 than at grade 4.

● When asked whether they had ever done experiments or projects using six common types of scientific materials and equipment, either in or out of school, only about one-third of eighth graders and about one-half of twelfth graders reported that they had used five or six of these materials in projects or experiments. These students had higher proficiency than did their grade-level counterparts who reported having used fewer than five of these types of materials.

● Despite the emphasis on "doing science" in most recommendations for science instruction, students in many high school science classrooms are not gaining extensive experience with laboratory activities. One-fourth of the high school seniors taking science courses reported that they never did experiments in their science classes and nearly 60 percent reported never working on science projects that took a week or more.

● Doing science homework is also not a prominent activity for many twelfth-grade science students — 41 percent reported never working on homework for their science class. However, twelfth-grade science students that spent more time on homework had higher proficiency than did their classmates who spent less time or did no science homework.

● Lecturing and the use of textbooks remain a mainstay in many science classrooms. Seventy-six percent of twelfth-grade science students and 61 percent of eighth-grade students reported that their teachers lecture in their science class at least several times a week, and nearly half of the eighth graders were taught by teachers who reported relying primarily on textbooks to determine what they teach.

● The nation's eighth graders are taught science by teachers who have an average of 12 years of experience teaching science. Almost all eighth graders were taught by teachers who had taken two or more college courses in biology; about two-thirds were taught by teachers who had taken two or more courses in chemistry; about 60 percent were taught by teachers who had taken two or more courses covering earth science, such as geology; and slightly more than half were taught by teachers who had taken two or more courses in physics. However, about three-fourths of the eighth graders were enrolled in earth or physical science classes, the content areas in which teachers reported taking the least college coursework.

* * * * * * *

The major results described above are discussed in more depth throughout this report. In addition, the report presents pertinent, detailed results regarding students' experiences in science and regarding their teachers' academic preparation and instructional practices in science classrooms. Throughout the report, students' average proficiency in science is reported in relation to a single variable at a time — however, it is important to note that proficiency may be influenced by many different factors acting in concert.

Chapter One summarizes overall average science achievement for the nation and demographic subpopulations on the NAEP science scale. The percentages of students in each grade who performed at or above four defined levels on the NAEP proficiency scale are discussed in Chapter Two. Chapter Three contains an examination of average proficiency in four science content areas and of the relationship between proficiency in those content areas and high school course-taking patterns in science. Chapter Four presents information about the priority schools place on science, students' attitudes toward science, and students' experiences with activities in science, both in and out of school. Chapter Five examines the relationship between instructional practices in science classrooms and student achievement, and Chapter 6 describes the demographic characteristics and academic preparation of eighth-grade students' science teachers.

Taken as a whole, this report provides a rich and detailed view of students' achievement and educational experiences in science that can serve as a foundation for further inquiry about the factors that affect student performance in science and a springboard for action required to improve science education in American schools.

OVERALL SCIENCE PROFICIENCY FOR THE NATION AND DEMOGRAPHIC SUBPOPULATIONS

*W*hat is the average science proficiency of fourth-, eighth- and twelfth-grade students in the United States? Are there differences in proficiency between male and female students or among students from different racial/ ethnic subpopulations? Does proficiency vary among students from different regions of the country or different types of communities? Does it vary with the level of education of students' parents? Is the proficiency of students attending public schools different from that of students attending private schools? This chapter of the report presents results for students at grades 4, 8, and 12 and for important demographic subpopulations of students at each grade.

To ensure that NAEP's science assessment was well balanced and that it reflected the goals and purposes of science education, a comprehensive development and review process was used to create a conceptual framework for the assessment. This framework defined three critical areas of science understanding:

- a grasp of the salient concepts in the three traditional content areas of science — the life sciences, physical sciences, and earth and space sciences;

- an awareness of the nature of science, encompassing scientific processes, the values and principles underlying scientific work, and the characteristics of scientific knowledge; and

- an ability to use scientific thinking skills, including knowing science, solving science problems, and conducting scientific inquiries.[6]

The assessment involved nationally representative samples of students at grades 4, 8, and 12, with approximately 6,500 students from public and private schools participating at each grade. Students' knowledge and understandings were measured using both multiple-choice and constructed-response questions, some of which required essays or short written responses and others which required students to mark or draw responses to indicate direction or location as well as to graph data.

The achievement results were analyzed using item response theory (IRT) scaling procedures, which allowed NAEP to estimate students' average proficiency on a scale ranging from 0 to 500. This science scale provides a way to compare achievement across grades and populations of students and to relate performance to a variety of home, school, and instructional factors. Throughout this report, differences in average proficiency or percentages of students were determined to be statistically significant at the .05 level using an application of the Bonferroni procedure. More detailed information on NAEP scaling procedures and the Bonferroni method can be found in Appendix A, which provides an overview of the procedures used in NAEP's 1990 science assessment. Definitions of student subpopulations can also be found in Appendix A.

AVERAGE SCIENCE PROFICIENCY FOR THE NATION: GRADES 4, 8, AND 12

TABLE 1.1 presents the average science proficiency of fourth-, eighth- and twelfth-grade students. On average, eighth graders performed 30 scale points higher than fourth graders, and twelfth graders performed 31 scale points higher than eighth graders.

[6] *Science Objectives, 1990 Assessment* (Princeton, NJ: National Assessment of Educational Progress, Educational Testing Service, 1989).

TABLE 1.1
Average Science Proficiency for the Nation

GRADE 4	GRADE 8	GRADE 12
233 (0.9)	263 (1.2)	294 (1.2)

The standard errors of the estimated proficiencies appear in parentheses. It can be said with 95 percent certainty that for each population of interest, the value for the whole population is within plus or minus two standard errors of the estimate for the sample.

The 1990 Science Report Card: NAEP's Assessment of Fourth, Eighth, and Twelfth Graders (National Center for Education Statistics, U.S. Department of Education, 1992).

AVERAGE SCIENCE PROFICIENCY

BY RACE/ETHNICITY Proficiency results for five racial/ethnic subpopulations are shown in FIGURE 1.1. There were large gaps in average proficiency between White students and Black students and between White students and Hispanic students at all three grades assessed. Also, the average proficiency of Hispanic students was higher than that of Black students at all three grades. At each grade, the difference in average proficiency between White students and Hispanic students was approximately 30 scale points, and the difference between White students and Black students was 37, 42, and 46 scale points at grades 4, 8, and 12, respectively. It is important to note, however, that these differences reflect averages for entire groups of students and that, in general, students from each racial/ethnic group were among both the higher and lower performers.

At all three grades, the proficiency of Asian/Pacific Islander students was not significantly different from that of White students, but was higher than that of Black students and Hispanic students. The average proficiency of fourth-grade American Indian students was lower than that of White and Asian/Pacific Islander fourth graders, but higher than the average proficiency of Black and Hispanic fourth graders. At grade 8, the performance of American Indian students was not significantly different from that of students in any of the other four racial/ethnic subgroups. At grade 12, their average proficiency was lower than that of White students, higher than the average proficiency of Black students, and not significantly different from the average proficiency of Asian/ Pacific Islander and Hispanic students.

FIGURE 1.1
Distribution of Students and
Average Science Proficiency by Race/Ethnicity

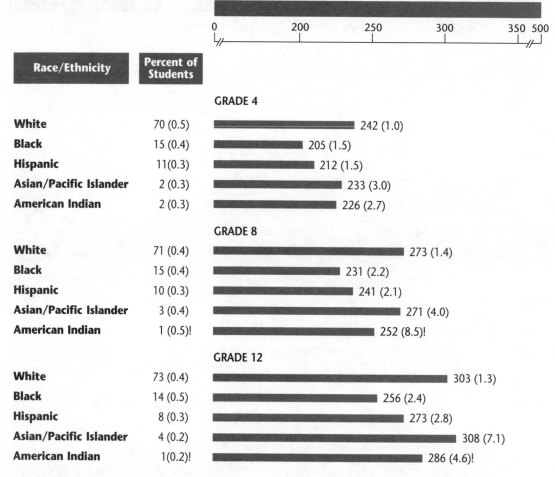

Race/Ethnicity	Percent of Students

GRADE 4

White	70 (0.5)	242 (1.0)
Black	15 (0.4)	205 (1.5)
Hispanic	11 (0.3)	212 (1.5)
Asian/Pacific Islander	2 (0.3)	233 (3.0)
American Indian	2 (0.3)	226 (2.7)

GRADE 8

White	71 (0.4)	273 (1.4)
Black	15 (0.4)	231 (2.2)
Hispanic	10 (0.3)	241 (2.1)
Asian/Pacific Islander	3 (0.4)	271 (4.0)
American Indian	1 (0.5)!	252 (8.5)!

GRADE 12

White	73 (0.4)	303 (1.3)
Black	14 (0.5)	256 (2.4)
Hispanic	8 (0.3)	273 (2.8)
Asian/Pacific Islander	4 (0.2)	308 (7.1)
American Indian	1 (0.2)!	286 (4.6)!

The standard errors of the estimated percentages and proficiencies appear in parentheses. It can be said with 95 percent certainty that for each population of interest, the value for the whole population is within plus or minus two standard errors of the estimate for the sample.

! Interpret with caution — the nature of the sample does not allow accurate determination of the variability of these estimated statistics.

The 1990 Science Report Card: NAEP's Assessment of Fourth, Eighth, and Twelfth Graders (National Center for Education Statistics, U.S. Department of Education, 1992).

AVERAGE SCIENCE PROFICIENCY

BY GENDER   The science proficiency results by gender presented in FIGURE 1.2 reveal that, on average, there was no gender difference in overall science proficiency at grade 4. However, at grades 8 and 12, small, but significant, differences in average proficiency existed between males and females, with males performing 4 scale points higher than females at grade 8, and 10 points higher at grade 12.

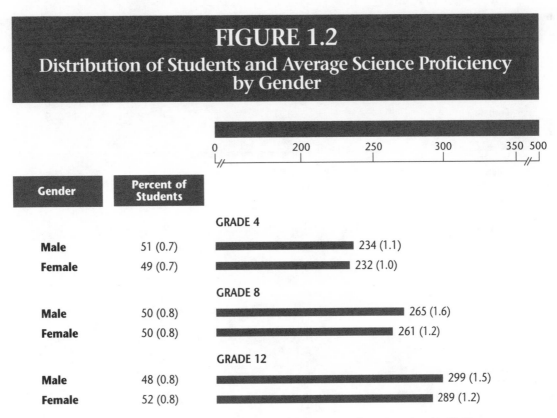

FIGURE 1.2
Distribution of Students and Average Science Proficiency by Gender

		0	200	250	300	350 500

Gender	Percent of Students	
		GRADE 4
Male	51 (0.7)	234 (1.1)
Female	49 (0.7)	232 (1.0)
		GRADE 8
Male	50 (0.8)	265 (1.6)
Female	50 (0.8)	261 (1.2)
		GRADE 12
Male	48 (0.8)	299 (1.5)
Female	52 (0.8)	289 (1.2)

The standard errors of the estimated percentages and proficiencies appear in parentheses. It can be said with 95 percent certainty that for each population of interest, the value for the whole population is within plus or minus two standard errors of the estimate for the sample.

The 1990 Science Report Card: NAEP's Assessment of Fourth, Eighth, and Twelfth Graders (National Center for Education Statistics, U.S. Department of Education, 1992).

Proficiency results by gender for White, Black, and Hispanic students, presented in TABLE 1.2, reflect the same general pattern as the national gender results. For each of the three racial/ethnic groups, there was virtually no difference in performance by gender at grade 4, but by grade 12 significant differences in performance emerged. At grade 12, across the racial/ethnic groups there was an 8 to 10 point gap between the average proficiency of males and that of females. These results suggest that Black and Hispanic females may be at a particular disadvantage as they leave high school to attend college, enter the work force, or join in other daily pursuits typical of our technologically oriented society.

TABLE 1.2
Distribution of Students and Average Science Proficiency by Race/Ethnicity and Gender

	Percent of Students	Average Proficiency
GRADE 4		
White		
Male	36 (0.7)	243 (1.3)
Female	34 (0.7)	241 (1.1)
Black		
Male	7 (0.3)	205 (1.8)
Female	8 (0.4)	206 (1.8)
Hispanic		
Male	6 (0.2)	213 (1.6)
Female	5 (0.2)	211 (1.9)
GRADE 8		
White		
Male	36 (0.8)	274 (1.8)
Female	35 (0.7)	271 (1.4)
Black		
Male	7 (0.3)	232 (2.9)
Female	8 (0.3)	230 (2.1)
Hispanic		
Male	5 (0.2)	243 (3.0)
Female	5 (0.2)	239 (2.5)
GRADE 12		
White		
Male	36 (0.8)	307 (1.5)
Female	37 (0.7)	298 (1.3)
Black		
Male	6 (0.4)	261 (2.7)
Female	8 (0.4)	253 (2.9)
Hispanic		
Male	4 (0.3)	278 (3.1)
Female	4 (0.3)	268 (3.5)

The standard errors of the estimated percentages and proficiencies appear in parentheses. It can be said with 95 percent certainty that for each population of interest, the value for the whole population is within plus or minus two standard errors of the estimate for the sample. Data are not presented for Asian/Pacific Islander or American Indian students because breakdown of these groups by gender resulted in too few students in each category.

The 1990 Science Report Card: NAEP's Assessment of Fourth, Eighth, and Twelfth Graders (National Center for Education Statistics, U.S. Department of Education, 1992).

AVERAGE SCIENCE PROFICIENCY

BY REGION There were no significant differences in average proficiency among students from the Northeast, Central, or West regions of the country at the three grade levels, as presented in TABLE 1.3. However, students from the Northeast had a significantly higher average proficiency than did students from the Southeast at all three grades. The average proficiency of students from the Southeast was also lower than that of students in the Central region at grades 8 and 12, and lower than that of students from the West region at grade 12.

TABLE 1.3
Distribution of Students and Average Science Proficiency by Region

	Percent of Students	Average Proficiency
GRADE 4		
Northeast	22 (0.8)	236 (1.9)
Southeast	24 (0.8)	227 (2.3)
Central	27 (0.8)	234 (2.2)
West	28 (0.8)	234 (2.0)
GRADE 8		
Northeast	21 (1.0)	269 (3.2)
Southeast	24 (0.8)	256 (2.0)
Central	25 (0.7)	265 (2.0)
West	30 (0.9)	263 (2.8)
GRADE 12		
Northeast	24 (1.0)	300 (3.3)
Southeast	21 (0.8)	279 (2.7)
Central	27 (0.5)	295 (2.0)
West	29 (0.9)	297 (2.9)

The standard errors of the estimated percentages and proficiencies appear in parentheses. It can be said with 95 percent certainty that for each population of interest, the value for the whole population is within plus or minus two standard errors of the estimate for the sample.

The 1990 Science Report Card: NAEP's Assessment of Fourth, Eighth, and Twelfth Graders (National Center for Education Statistics, U.S. Department of Education, 1992).

AVERAGE SCIENCE PROFICIENCY BY TYPE OF COMMUNITY   Results that relate students' science proficiency to the types of communities in which they attend school present an opportunity to monitor the link between community socioeconomic circumstances and educational performance. TABLE 1.4 shows average science proficiency for students attending school in three extreme community types — advantaged urban, disadvantaged urban, and extreme rural — as well as the average proficiency of students in types of communities other than these three. (Criteria for defining each of these community types are described in Appendix A.)

TABLE 1.4

Distribution of Students and
Average Science Proficiency by Type of Community

	Percent of Students	Average Proficiency
GRADE 4		
Advantaged Urban	11 (1.7)	252 (2.4)
Disadvantaged Urban	9 (1.1)	209 (2.6)
Extreme Rural	11 (1.8)	235 (2.6)
Other	69 (2.8)	233 (1.0)
GRADE 8		
Advantaged Urban	10 (2.2)!	283 (4.1)!
Disadvantaged Urban	9 (1.7)	242 (4.2)
Extreme Rural	11 (2.1)	257 (3.2)
Other	69 (2.8)	264 (1.5)
GRADE 12		
Advantaged Urban	10 (2.4)!	304 (4.4)!
Disadvantaged Urban	12 (2.5)	273 (5.3)
Extreme Rural	11 (2.7)!	291 (3.9)!
Other	67 (3.5)	296 (1.6)

The standard errors of the estimated percentages and proficiencies appear in parentheses. It can be said with 95 percent certainty that for each population of interest, the value for the whole population is within plus or minus two standard errors of the estimate for the sample.

! Interpret with caution — the nature of the sample does not allow accurate determrnination of the variability of these estimated statistics.

The 1990 Science Report Card: NAEP's Assessment of Fourth, Eighth, and Twelfth Graders (National Center for Education Statistics, U.S. Department of Education, 1992).

At all three grades, students attending schools in disadvantaged urban communities had lower average science proficiency than did those in advantaged urban, extreme rural, and other types of communities. Also, at grades 4 and 8, students from advantaged urban communities performed better than students from extreme rural or other types of communities. There were no significant differences in performance, however, between students attending school in extreme rural communities and those in types of communities classified as "other" at any of the three grade levels.

A V E R A G E   S C I E N C E   P R O F I C I E N C Y

B Y   T Y P E   O F   S C H O O L   The results in TABLE 1.5 summarize average proficiency for students attending public schools, Catholic schools, and other types of private schools. At grades 4 and 8, students attending Catholic or other private schools outperformed those attending public schools by approximately 10 to 14 scale points, on average. However, at grade 12, public-school students' average proficiency was approximately equal to that of students in Catholic and other private schools. There were no significant differences in average proficiency between Catholic-school students and students attending other private schools at any grade level.

TABLE 1.5
Distribution of Students and Average Science Proficiency by Type of School

	Percent of Students	Average Proficiency
GRADE 4		
Public Schools	89 (1.1)	231 (1.0)
Catholic Schools	7 (0.9)	241 (2.0)
Other Private Schools	5 (0.7)	247 (3.1)
GRADE 8		
Public Schools	89 (1.3)	262 (1.4)
Catholic Schools	7 (1.1)	276 (1.9)
Other Private Schools	4 (0.7)	274 (3.9)
GRADE 12		
Public Schools	90 (1.4)	293 (1.3)
Catholic Schools	5 (1.1)	301 (3.4)
Other Private Schools	4 (1.0)	302 (4.9)

The standard errors of the estimated percentages and proficiencies appear in parentheses. It can be said with 95 percent certainty that for each population of interest, the value for the whole population is within plus or minus two standard errors of the estimate for the sample.

The 1990 Science Report Card: NAEP's Assessment of Fourth, Eighth, and Twelfth Graders (National Center for Education Statistics, U.S. Department of Education, 1992).

AVERAGE SCIENCE PROFICIENCY BY PARENTS' HIGHEST LEVEL OF EDUCATION   In addition to collecting information about basic demographic characteristics, NAEP obtained data from students regarding various home and school background factors that could play a prominent role in influencing educational achievement. TABLE 1.6 displays assessment results by the highest level of education reported for either parent. It should be noted that at grade 4, 35 percent of the students did not know the education level of either parent.

At all three grades, students whose parents had at least some education beyond high school had higher average proficiency than those whose parents had no education beyond high school. Similarly, at grades 8 and 12, students whose parents had graduated from college had a higher proficiency, on average, than did students in the other three groups. For students in the higher two grade levels, there was a significant increase in proficiency with each increase in the level of parents' education.

TABLE 1.6
Distribution of Students and Average Science Proficiency by Parents' Highest Level of Education

	Percent of Students	Average Proficiency
GRADE 4		
Did Not Finish HS	5 (0.4)	221 (2.2)
Graduated From HS	16 (0.7)	226 (1.4)
Some Education After HS	9 (0.4)	242 (1.8)
Graduated From College	35 (1.1)	243 (1.2)
GRADE 8		
Did Not Finish HS	9 (0.6)	241 (2.3)
Graduated From HS	25 (0.8)	254 (1.3)
Some Education After HS	19 (0.8)	268 (1.4)
Graduated From College	40 (1.6)	276 (1.7)
GRADE 12		
Did Not Finish HS	8 (0.6)	269 (2.5)
Graduated From HS	24 (0.8)	279 (1.3)
Some Education After HS	26 (0.8)	295 (1.3)
Graduated From College	40 (1.3)	308 (1.4)

The standard errors of the estimated percentages and proficiencies appear in parentheses. It can be said with 95 percent certainty that for each population of interest, the value for the whole population is within plus or minus two standard errors of the estimate for the sample. Within each grade, percentages of students do not total 100 percent because some students did not know their parents' highest level of education.

The 1990 Science Report Card: NAEP's Assessment of Fourth, Eighth, and Twelfth Graders (National Center for Education Statistics, U.S. Department of Education, 1992).

AVERAGE SCIENCE PROFICIENCY BY ADDITIONAL FACTORS RELATED TO THE HOME TABLE 1.7 presents average science proficiency results according to a number of school and home factors that have been related to academic achievement.

For all grades, students who had access to a greater number of types of reading materials at home (i.e., books, magazines, newspapers, an encyclopedia) had higher average science proficiency than did students with access to fewer types of materials. Also, at all three grade levels, students who read 6 to 10 or more than 10 pages for school and homework each day performed significantly better than those who read 5 or fewer pages. At grade 12, students who reported reading more than 10 pages daily had higher average achievement than students who read 6 to 10 pages.

TABLE 1.7
Distribution of Students and Average Science Proficiency by Additional Factors Related to the Home

	GRADE 4		GRADE 8		GRADE 12	
	Percent of Students	Average Proficiency	Percent of Students	Average Proficiency	Percent of Students	Average Proficiency
Types of Reading Materials in the Home						
Zero to two types	34 (1.0)	222 (1.1)	20 (0.7)	241 (1.7)	14 (0.7)	272 (1.9)
Three types	34 (0.7)	235 (1.1)	30 (0.8)	260 (1.2)	27 (0.8)	289 (1.5)
Four types	33 (0.9)	244 (1.0)	50 (0.9)	274 (1.5)	59 (1.0)	301 (1.3)
Daily Amount of Time Spent on Homework — All Subjects						
None assigned	21 (1.3)	237 (1.5)	6 (0.5)	249 (3.6)	12 (0.7)	273 (1.6)
Did not do it	5 (0.3)	215 (1.7)	7 (0.5)	245 (2.3)	9 (0.4)	292 (2.8)
One-half hour or less	34 (1.1)	233 (1.2)	20 (0.7)	261 (1.9)	21 (0.6)	295 (1.6)
One hour	24 (0.7)	237 (1.3)	40 (0.8)	268 (1.3)	32 (0.7)	296 (1.3)
Two hours	17 (0.8)	228 (1.4)	19 (0.6)	268 (1.7)	18 (0.8)	299 (1.8)
More than two hours	—	—	8 (0.5)	265 (3.0)	9 (0.5)	303 (2.4)
Daily Pages Read for School and Homework — All Subjects						
Five or fewer pages	26 (0.8)	226 (1.1)	32 (0.9)	253 (1.6)	33 (1.1)	281 (1.5)
Six to 10 pages	21 (0.7)	234 (1.3)	28 (0.6)	266 (1.5)	24 (0.8)	292 (1.3)
More than 10 pages	53 (1.1)	236 (1.1)	40 (1.0)	271 (1.6)	43 (1.3)	304 (1.5)
Days of School Missed last Month						
None	—	—	44 (0.8)	269 (1.1)	30 (0.9)	300 (1.4)
One or two days	—	—	33 (0.6)	268 (1.6)	38 (0.6)	297 (1.7)
Three days or more	—	—	23 (0.6)	249 (1.8)	32 (0.8)	285 (1.6)
Parents Living in Home						
Both parents	75 (0.8)	238 (1.0)	77 (0.6)	270 (1.3)	75 (0.7)	300 (1.1)
Single parent	20 (0.7)	222 (1.3)	19 (0.6)	251 (1.7)	20 (0.7)	286 (1.9)
Neither parent	5 (0.4)	205 (2.2)	4 (0.3)	231(3.9)	5 (0.3)	274 (3.6)
Daily Hours of Television Viewing						
Zero to one hour	18 (0.7)	235 (1.3)	14 (0.6)	273 (2.7)	34 (1.1)	304 (1.7)
Two hours	19 (0.6)	242 (1.4)	22 (0.8)	271 (2.1)	27 (0.6)	296 (1.5)
Three hours	16 (0.5)	238 (1.4)	22 (0.5)	267 (1.2)	19 (0.6)	291 (1.5)
Four to five hours	21 (0.6)	236 (1.2)	28 (0.8)	260 (1.3)	15 (0.7)	279 (1.7)
Six hours or more	26 (0.7)	219 (1.2)	14 (0.5)	241 (1.9)	5 (0.4)	263 (2.7)

The standard errors of the estimated percentages and proficiencies appear in parentheses. It can be said with 95 percent certainty that for each population of interest, the value for the whole population is within plus or minus two standard errors of the estimate for the sample.

The 1990 Science Report Card: NAEP's Assessment of Fourth, Eighth, and Twelfth Graders (National Center for Education Statistics, U.S. Department of Education, 1992).

Fourth-grade students who reported spending at least one hour or even one-half hour or less on homework for all of their subjects each day performed significantly better than those who had been assigned homework but did not do it. However, those fourth graders who completed one hour or less of homework also outperformed students who spent two hours on homework. This difference may be due in part to the fact that teachers often assign more homework to those students who might benefit from additional work. The difference may also result from higher-performing students completing their homework in less time than lower-performing students. It also should be noted that 21 percent of fourth graders reported that they had no homework assigned to them.

At grade 8, there were no differences in average science proficiency among students who spent more than two hours, two hours, or one hour on all their homework each day, but students who spent one or two hours on homework performed better than those who only did homework for one-half hour or less. At grade 12, there were no differences in performance among students who reported spending more than two hours, two hours, one hour, or one-half hour or less on homework.

Average proficiency results for another school variable — the number of days of school missed in the month prior to the assessment — indicated that students in grades 8 and 12 who missed none or only one or two days of school during that month performed better than did students who missed three or more days. Significant proficiency differences were also found in relation to another factor — the number of parents living in the home. At all three grades, students who had both parents living at home had higher average proficiency than students who had one parent living at home, who, in turn had higher proficiency than students who had neither parent living at home.

Students were also asked how many hours they spent watching television each day. At grades 8 and 12, there was a general decline in average science proficiency with increased amounts of time spent watching television. Students who reported watching television six or more hours each day had lower average proficiency than students in the groups reporting that they watched five hours or less, and eighth- and twelfth-grade students who watched four or five hours each day had lower proficiency than students in groups who reported watching television for three hours or less. This pattern was not as evident at grade 4, although students who watched six or more hours of television daily did have lower average proficiency than those who watched for less than six hours.

AVERAGE PROFICIENCY BY TYPE OF HIGH SCHOOL PROGRAM AND PLANS AFTER HIGH SCHOOL As shown in TABLE 1.8, at grade 12, the type of high school program in which students were enrolled and their plans after graduation were directly related to their average science proficiency. Twelfth graders who were enrolled in academic programs had substantially higher average proficiency than did those enrolled in either general or vocational/technical programs. Also, on average, students enrolled in general programs outperformed those in vocational/technical curricula. Consistent with the results for type of high school program, high school seniors planning to attend a four-year college had considerably higher average science proficiency than those who planned to work full-time, attend a two-year college or vocational, technical, or business school, or who had other plans after graduation.

TABLE 1.8
Distribution of Students and Average Science Proficiency by Type of High School Program and Plans after High School Graduation

TYPE OF HIGH-SCHOOL PROGRAM:

ACADEMIC		GENERAL		VOCATIONAL/TECHNICAL	
Percent of Students	Average Proficiency	Percent of Students	Average Proficiency	Percent of Students	Average Proficiency
57 (1.3)	309 (1.3)	34 (1.1)	277 (1.4)	8 (0.6)	265 (2.4)

PLANS AFTER HIGH SCHOOL:

WORKING FULL-TIME		2-YR COLLEGE OR VOC/TECH/BUS. SCHOOL		4-YR COLLEGE OR SERVICE ACADEMY		OTHER	
Percent of Students	Average Proficiency	Percent of Students	Average Proficiency	Percent of Students	Average Proficiency	Percent of Students	Average Proficiency
14 (0.6)	274 (1.8)	25 (1.0)	278 (1.5)	53 (1.2)	311 (1.3)	8 (0.4)	279 (2.4)

The standard errors of the estimated percentages and proficiencies appear in parentheses. It can be said with 95 percent certainty that for each population of interest, the value for the whole population is within plus or minus two standard errors of the estimate for the sample.

The 1990 Science Report Card: NAEP's Assessment of Fourth, Eighth, and Twelfth Graders (National Center for Education Statistics, U.S. Department of Education, 1992).

TABLE 1.9
Percentage of Students within Selected Demographic Subgroups in the Top One-Third of the Schools and the Bottom One-Third of the Schools

	PERCENTAGE OF STUDENTS BY RACE/ETHNICITY					PERCENTAGE OF STUDENTS BY TYPE OF COMMUNITY			
GRADE 4	White	Black	Hispanic	Asian/ Pacific Islander	American Indian	Adv. Urban	Disadv. Urban	Extreme Rural	Other
Top One-Third	38 (3.2)	8 (1.8)	15 (2.3)	25 (9.7)	27 (6.0)	69 (9.3)	4 (2.4)	17 (4.6)	31 (3.2)
Bottom One-Third	18 (2.2)	73 (3.9)	53 (3.4)	39 (9.0)	33 (4.7)	4 (1.7)	78 (5.7)	19 (8.5)	30 (2.8)
GRADE 8									
Top One-Third	31 (3.5)	11 (2.3)	13 (2.5)	36 (7.7)	15 (11.8)!	70 (12.6)!	3 (0.7)	17 (6.5)	24 (2.8)
Bottom One-Third	25 (3.4)	69 (4.7)	59 (5.9)	33 (8.5)	59 (26.9)!	5 (3.8)!	81 (8.6)	58 (12.4)	31 (3.9)
GRADE 12									
Top One-Third	41 (3.8)	13 (3.3)	22 (4.4)	37 (15.4)	29 (8.4)!	65 (9.7)!	14 (6.3)	29 (7.1)!	36 (4.6)
Bottom One-Third	16 (3.6)	64 (4.6)	47 (6.8)	17 (5.9)	28 (11.2)!	16 (6.7)!	64 (9.3)	28 (9.7)!	19 (3.5)

	PERCENTAGE OF STUDENTS BY REGION				PERCENTAGE OF STUDENTS BY PARENTS' EDUCATION			
GRADE 4	North-East	South-East	Central	West	Less than HS	Grad. HS	Some Ed. After HS	Grad. College
Top One-Third	46 (4.3)	15 (5.0)	25 (6.9)	39 (5.5)	17 (3.1)	23 (3.0)	30 (3.4)	42 (3.3)
Bottom One-Third	24 (2.1)	49 (6.5)	20 (4.4)	29 (3.7)	47 (4.3)	32 (2.8)	28 (3.1)	25 (2.3)
GRADE 8								
Top One-Third	40 (6.6)	14 (4.0)	26 (4.3)	26 (7.3)	9 (1.8)	18 (2.3)	26 (3.5)	37 (4.5)
Bottom One-Third	18 (6.8)	53 (5.9)	23 (4.3)	45 (8.0)	63 (4.4)	41 (3.8)	33 (3.4)	25 (3.3)
GRADE 12								
Top One-Third	50 (7.8)	6 (2.1)	37 (6.6)	43 (7.9)	14 (2.5)	26 (2.9)	33 (3.7)	48 (4.0)
Bottom One-Third	17 (4.6)	47 (9.4)	18 (6.7)	24 (5.8)	51 (6.4)	32 (3.8)	26 (3.8)	16 (2.4)

The standard errors of the estimated percentages appear in parentheses. It can be said with 95 percent certainty that for each population of interest, the value for the whole population is within plus or minus two standard errors of the estimate for the sample.

! Interpret with caution — the nature of the sample does not allow accurate determination of the variability of these estimated statistics.

The 1990 Science Report Card: NAEP's Assessment of Fourth, Eighth, and Twelfth Graders (National Center for Education Statistics, U.S. Department of Education, 1992).

NAEP identified the top one-third and the bottom one-third of the schools based on students' average science proficiency by school, and then examined the characteristics of students attending those schools with regard to race/ethnicity, type of community, region, and parents' highest level of education. TABLE 1.9 presents the percentages of students from demographic subgroups who attended the top one-third and the bottom one-third performing schools.

As might be anticipated based on the average proficiency results across racial/ethnic subpopulations, at all three grades approximately 30 to 40 percent of White students and 25 to 40 percent of Asian/Pacific Islander students attended schools that ranked in the top one-third based on average science performance, compared to the approximately 10 to 15 percent of Black students and 15 to 20 percent of Hispanic students who attended these schools. Also, approximately 65 to 75 percent of Black students attended schools in the lower-performing one-third.

At all three grades, 65 to 70 percent of students from advantaged urban communities attended the top one-third schools. In comparison, approximately 65 to 80 percent of students from disadvantaged urban communities attended the bottom one-third schools. The results by region and by parents' highest level of education also reflect the average proficiency results for the nation. At each of the three grade levels, the percentages of students from the Northeast attending the top one-third schools was significantly higher than the percentages of students from the Southeast who attended those schools. Also, significantly higher percentages of students whose parents had graduated from college attended the top one-third schools than did those students whose parents had no further education beyond high school.

Performance distributions by percentile for fourth-, eighth-, and twelfth-grade students are presented in TABLE 1.10. These results serve to emphasize the tremendous range in student performance on the assessment within each grade. At grade 4, the lowest performing 10 percent of the students had proficiency of 191 or below, while the top 10 percent of fourth graders had proficiency of 272 or above, which was roughly comparable to the median proficiency for eighth graders (265). Additionally, the top 10 percent of fourth graders performed better than the bottom 25 percent of twelfth graders.

Great variation in proficiency also occurred at grade 8, where nearly 25 percent of the students had proficiencies at or below the median proficiency of fourth graders (234), and nearly another 25 percent had proficiencies at or above the median for twelfth graders (291). At grade 12, one-fourth of the students performed at or below the median proficiency for grade 8 (265), and about 10 percent performed at or below a level similar to the median for fourth graders — 234. The top 10 percent of the twelfth graders, however, performed at or above the 350 level, indicating some in-depth science understanding among the top-performing high-school seniors.

TABLE 1.10
Percentiles of Average Science Proficiency at Grades 4, 8, and 12

	5th Percentile	10th Percentile	25th Percentile	50th Percentile	75th Percentile	90th Percentile	95th Percentile
Grade 4	179 (1.3)	191 (1.2)	212 (1.1)	234 (1.5)	255 (1.2)	272 (1.1)	282 (1.4)
Grade 8	195 (2.2)	210 (1.8)	237 (1.4)	265 (1.4)	291 (1.5)	313 (1.8)	324 (2.2)
Grade 12	222 (1.8)	238 (1.9)	265 (1.6)	294 (1.2)	323 (1.1)	349 (1.7)	362 (1.7)

The standard errors of the estimated proficiencies appear in parentheses. It can be said with 95 percent certainty that for each population of interest, the value for the whole population is within plus or minus two standard errors of the estimate for the sample.

The 1990 Science Report Card: NAEP's Assessment of Fourth, Eighth, and Twelfth Graders (National Center for Education Statistics, U.S. Department of Education, 1992).

S U M M A R Y   Results from the 1990 NAEP science assessment revealed many significant differences in achievement among major demographic subpopulations. At all three grades, White students, Asian/Pacific Islander students, and Hispanic students had higher proficiency, on average, than Black students. In general, the average proficiency of White and Asian/Pacific Islander students was significantly higher than that of Hispanic students.

No gender difference in average science achievement existed at grade 4; however, small, but significant, differences favoring males were evident at grades 8 and 12. Average proficiency results by region of the country showed that students from the Northeast performed better than students from the Southeast at all three grades. At grade 12, students from the Southeast had lower proficiency than twelfth graders from each of the other three regions.

Student proficiency in science was also related to socioeconomic factors. Students from advantaged urban communities had higher average proficiency than their grade-level counterparts from disadvantaged urban communities, and, in general, students whose parents had more education performed better than students whose parents had less education.

Several additional home and school variables were also related to differences in students' achievement. In general, at all three grades, students with access to a greater number of types of reading materials at home had higher average science achievement than students with fewer available types of reading materials. Also, in general, fourth- and eighth-grade students who did their homework had higher proficiency than those who did not do their assigned homework. At all three grade levels, students who read more for school and homework had higher average proficiency than did students who read less. In contrast, students who watched more than six hours of television each day had significantly lower science proficiency, on average, than those who watched less television. Students who missed two or fewer days of school in the month preceding the assessment performed better than those who had missed three days or more. In addition, students living with both parents had higher average proficiency than did students living with one parent, who, in turn, performed better than students living apart from both parents.

At grade 12, average proficiency was related to students' type of high school program and their plans after high school. High school seniors in academic programs had higher average science proficiency than those in general or vocational/technical programs, and students who planned on attending a four-year college after high-school graduation performed better than those who had other types of plans after high school.

These results support several themes prevalent in the science reform literature. One such dominant theme, clearly expressed in Project 2061's *Science for All Americans*, is that race, sex, or economic circumstances must no longer be permitted to be factors in determining who does and who does not receive a good education in science.[7] According to that report, "to neglect the science education of any (as has happened too often to girls and minority students) is to deprive them of a basic education, handicap them for life, and deprive the nation of talented workers and informed citizens — a loss the nation can ill afford."

---

[7] *Science for All Americans: A Project 2061 Report on Literacy Goals in Science, Mathematics, and Technology* (Washington, D.C.: American Association for the Advancement of Science, 1989).

Educating Americans for the 21st Century: A Report to the American People and the National Science Board (Washington, D.C.: National Science Board Commission on Precollege Education in Science, Mathematics, and Technology, 1983).

The NAEP results, however, show large performance discrepancies for Black and Hispanic students and students attending disadvantaged urban schools as well as a gender gap that appears to emerge as part of school science education.

Along parallel lines, the numerous advocates for scientific literacy for all Americans point out that science can no longer be reserved for the elite or college-bound. Students who expect to join the workforce immediately after high school also need a strong base of scientific knowledge beyond that provided by a narrow focus on trade skills.[8] Here again, the NAEP findings suggest large gaps in science achievement between college-bound seniors and their classmates with other types of post-high-school plans. Twelfth graders in vocational/technical high-school programs had particularly low achievement, performing at about the same level as the median proficiency for eighth grade.

Finally, these results tend to confirm the importance of an emphasis on academic learning in the home.[9] The vast majority of students spend a disproportionate amount of time watching television as opposed to reading or doing homework. Parents can play a critical role in strengthening their children's education by exercising the supervision necessary to ensure regular school attendance, completion of homework assignments, and time spent reading rather than watching television.

[8] Carnegie Council on Adolescent Development, *Turning Points: Preparing American Youth for the 21st Century* (New York, NY: Carnegie Corporation of New York, 1989).

[9] James P. Comer, "Home, School, and Academic Learning," in *Access to Knowledge: An Agenda for Our Nation's Schools,* John T. Goodlad and Pamela Keating, Eds. (New York, NY: College Entrance Examination Board, 1990).

The Harvard Education Letter, *Parents and Schools* (Cambridge, MA: Harvard University Press, November/ December 1988).

What Works: Research About Teaching and Learning, Second Edition (Washington, D.C.: U.S. Department of Education, 1987).

*L*EVELS OF SCIENCE PROFICIENCY FOR THE NATION AND DEMOGRAPHIC SUBPOPULATIONS

LEVELS OF SCIENCE PROFICIENCY

*T*he data presented in Chapter One provide information about overall science achievement for the nation's fourth-, eighth-, and twelfth-grade students and for important demographic subpopulations at each of these grades. However, average proficiency values alone do not provide information about the range of science knowledge and skills possessed by students. What types of assessment questions can typically be answered correctly by students with an average proficiency of 200? What additional skills and understandings distinguish an average science proficiency of 300 from an average proficiency of 250? In order to answer questions such as these and provide a basis for describing students' science knowledge and skills as measured by NAEP's 0 to 500 science scale, descriptions of four levels of science proficiency were developed (200, 250, 300 and 350). In theory, NAEP could have defined proficiency levels above 350 or below 200; however, so few students in the assessment performed at the extreme ends of the 0 to 500 scale that it was not useful to do so. For example, descriptions of five levels of proficiency (150, 200, 250, 300, and 350) were developed and reported for the 1986 NAEP science assessment and the 1990 NAEP science trend assessment. However, the results for the 1990 NAEP cross-sectional assessment, described in this report, revealed that nearly all students in each grade performed at or above Level 150 proficiency. Therefore, in this report, example items and results for proficiency levels are presented only for Levels 200, 250, 300, and 350.

The four levels of science proficiency are described in FIGURE 2.1. The descriptions were developed to provide information about the types of questions that were answered correctly by students at one level on the scale and how these differ from the questions answered correctly by students at the next lower level. The descriptions summarizing performance at the four levels were originally developed subsequent to NAEP's 1986 science assessment. At that time, sets of anchor items — one set for each level — were delineated and studied by a panel of science specialists, who carefully considered and articulated the overarching types of knowledge, skills, and reasoning abilities demonstrated by correct responses to the questions in each set. For the present report, NAEP repeated the process of delineating sets of anchor items based on the 1990 assessment item pool and data to verify that the general descriptions were still appropriate. As illustrated in this chapter and in Appendix B, the anchor questions for the 1990 assessment fit the general descriptions developed for 1986 with only slight modifications. (A more complete description of the empirical analysis underlying this scale-anchoring process is included in Appendix B.)

FIGURE 2.1
Levels of Science Proficiency

LEVEL 200 UNDERSTANDS SIMPLE SCIENTIFIC PRINCIPLES

Students at this level are developing some understanding of simple scientific principles, particularly in the life sciences. For example, they exhibit some rudimentary knowledge of the structure and function of plants and animals.

LEVEL 250 APPLIES GENERAL SCIENTIFIC INFORMATION

Students at this level can interpret data from simple tables and make inferences about the outcomes of experimental procedures. They exhibit knowledge and understanding of the life sciences, including a familiarity with some aspects of animal behavior and of ecological relationships. These students also demonstrate some knowledge of basic information from the physical sciences.

LEVEL 300 ANALYZES SCIENTIFIC PROCEDURES AND DATA

Students at this level can evaluate the appropriateness of the design of an experiment. They have more detailed scientific knowledge and the skill to apply their knowledge in interpreting information from text and graphs. These students also exhibit a growing understanding of principles from the physical sciences.

LEVEL 350 INTEGRATES SPECIALIZED SCIENTIFIC INFORMATION

Students at this level can infer relationships and draw conclusions using detailed scientific knowledge from the physical sciences, particularly chemistry. They also can apply basic principles of genetics and interpret the societal implications of research in this field.

Student performance at each of the proficiency levels results from an interaction between the understanding of facts, concepts, and principles and the reasoning ability to apply knowledge to novel situations, infer relationships, evaluate experimental designs, and integrate various types and sources of information. The arrangement of the levels of proficiency on a hierarchical scale does not necessarily imply that the knowledge and skills described in successive levels are acquired by students in a hierarchical manner, but the descriptions associated with the proficiency levels do describe the knowledge and skills that are *typical* of the *groups* of students who performed at successively higher levels of proficiency.

LEVELS OF SCIENCE PROFICIENCY FOR THE NATION:

GRADES 4, 8, AND 12   The percentages of fourth-, eighth-, and twelfth-grade students who performed at or above each of the four proficiency levels are displayed in FIGURE 2.2.

At grade 4, 85 percent of the students performed at or above Level 200, demonstrating a consistent grasp of the knowledge of basic facts and principles typical of performance at this level, and 31 percent performed at or above Level 250. As might be expected, because students at this grade level have not encountered the full range of material encompassed by the NAEP science scale, very few (1 percent) performed at or above Level 300 and virtually no fourth graders reached Level 350.

At the eighth grade, substantial percentages of students performed at or above the lower two proficiency levels, with 94 percent and 64 percent attaining Levels 200 and 250 respectively. However, only small percentages of eighth graders attained the two higher proficiency levels, despite the fact that many new eighth-grade curriculum frameworks call for beginning development of the understandings and reasoning skills typified by performance at these two levels.[10] Eighteen percent of eighth graders performed at or above Level 300, and 1 percent reached Level 350.

Nearly all twelfth-grade students (99 percent) demonstrated the basic knowledge characteristic of Level 200, and 84 percent performed at or above Level 250, showing a consistent ability to apply simple scientific information. However, fewer than half of these students (45 percent) performed at or above Level 300 and fewer than one in ten students

[10] Bill G. Aldridge, *Essential Changes in Secondary School Science: Scope, Sequence, and Coordination* (Washington, D.C.: National Science Teachers Association, 1989).

Earth Science Education for the 21st Century: a Planning Guide (Alexandria, VA: American Geologic Institute, 1991).

Rodger W. Bybee, et al., *Science and Technology Education for the Middle Years: Frameworks for Curriculum and Instruction* (Washington, D.C.: The National Center for Improving Science Education, 1990).

(9 percent) attained Level 350. These results support the findings from the 1990 NAEP science trend assessment,[11] and show that most eighth-and twelfth-grade students know some basic scientific facts and principles. However, especially considering the technological needs of today's society, a disproportionately low percentage of these students possess in-depth scientific knowledge or the ability to accomplish even relatively straightforward tasks requiring application or thinking skills.

FIGURE 2.2
Percentages of Students at or above
Four Proficiency Levels on the NAEP Science Scale

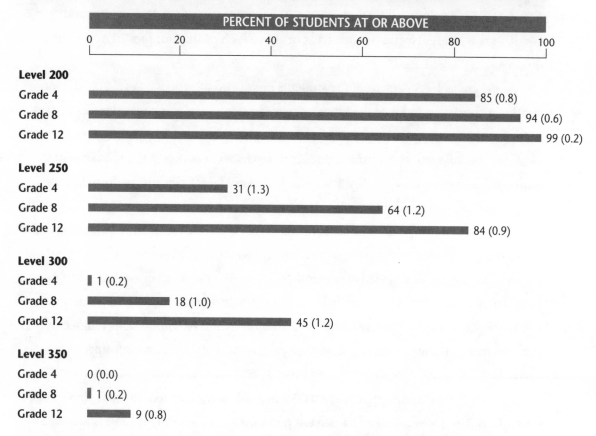

The standard errors of the estimated percentages appear in parentheses. It can be said with 95 percent certainty that for each population of interest, the value for the whole population is within plus or minus two standard errors of the estimate for the sample. When the percentage of students is either 0 or 100, the standard error is inestimable. However, percentages 99.5 percent and greater were rounded to 100 percent and percentages less than 0.5 percent were rounded to 0 percent.

The 1990 Science Report Card: NAEP's Assessment of Fourth, Eighth, and Twelfth Graders (National Center for Education Statistics, U.S. Department of Education, 1992).

---

[11] Ina V.S. Mullis, et al., *Trends in Academic Progress: Achievement of U.S. Students in Science, 1969-70 to 1990; Mathematics, 1973 to 1990; Reading, 1971 to 1990; and Writing, 1984 to 1990* (Washington, D.C.: U.S. Department of Education, 1991).

EXAMPLES OF ANCHOR ITEMS
FOR THE FOUR LEVELS
OF SCIENCE PROFICIENCY   This section provides examples of 25
scale-anchor items from the 1990 science assessment. These items were likely to be
answered correctly by students performing at the given level of proficiency and much less
likely to be answered by students performing at the next lower proficiency level. The
specific criteria used to define anchor items for each level of proficiency are described in
Appendix B. The illustrative questions presented in this chapter are intended to exemplify
the content and skills that are typical of performance at a given proficiency level, but they
do not cover the entire spectrum of anchor items for each level or the range of content
and skills covered by the 1990 science assessment. Additional anchor items are presented
in Appendix B, although some anchor items are kept secure for use in future assessments
to monitor trends in science performance.

Each example item is accompanied by results for each grade at which the item was
administered. The results include the overall percentage of students who answered the
item correctly and the percentage of students performing at or near each proficiency level
who answered the item correctly (see "Percent Correct for Anchor Levels"). For example,
for the first item shown for Level 200, 79 percent of the fourth graders answered the
question correctly. Of the fourth graders whose proficiency was at or near Level 200, 69
percent answered the item correctly. In addition, 92 percent of the students who performed at or near Level 250 and 98 percent of the students at or near Level 300 also
answered the question correctly. Because the NAEP science scale encompasses content
typically covered across the entire elementary and secondary school curricula, it would be
unlikely (but not impossible) for many fourth-grade students to have performed at the
higher range of the scale. Because virtually no fourth-grade students performed at or above
Level 350, results for the sample questions are not listed at that level.

The percentage of students reaching a particular level is the percentage that
achieved at or above that level. For example, the percentage of fourth graders performing
at or above 200, 85 percent, as shown in FIGURE 2.2, represents the proportion of
students in the population that would have received a score of 200 or better on the
hypothetical 500-item test represented by the 0 to 500 NAEP science scale. In comparison,
for the first example question, 69 percent of the students who achieved at about Level 200
answered this item correctly, while 79 percent of all students at all levels of achievement
answered the item correctly. Because the percentage of students attaining a particular
anchor level is based on overall achievement, and the percentage of students correctly
answering a particular question illustrating that anchor level is based only on

achievement for that item, the two percentages provide different types of information and generally will not be the same. Therefore, when discussing overall performance, the information in Figure 2.2 is most useful, but for discussing performance on individual items, the percentages shown with each item should be used.

LEVEL 200 —
UNDERSTANDS SIMPLE
SCIENTIFIC PRINCIPLES The example assessment items for Level 200 suggest that students performing at or above this level are developing an understanding of some basic scientific facts and principles in the life sciences, such as knowing that animals must breathe oxygen to stay alive and knowing that a snake has dry skin and hatches from an egg. These students also were able to recognize similarities and differences among organisms, as exemplified by the "grasshopper-wasp" and "animal tracks" questions. In addition, these students were typically able to read a simple bar graph.

EXAMPLE: LEVEL 200

The organism above is most closely related to which of the following?

A

B

C

D

EXAMPLE: LEVEL 200

Grade 4: 80% Correct Overall					Grade 8: 93% Correct Overall			
Percent Correct for Anchor Levels					Percent Correct for Anchor Levels			
200	250	300	350		200	250	300	350
68	92	99	—		84	95	98	100

Which of the following gases must an animal breathe in order to remain alive?

A Helium

B Hydrogen

C Nitrogen

(D) Oxygen

EXAMPLE: LEVEL 200

Grade 4: 70% Correct Overall					Grade 8: 80% Correct Overall			
Percent Correct for Anchor Levels					Percent Correct for Anchor Levels			
200	250	300	350		200	250	300	350
62	79	86	—		67	78	89	92

A small animal with dry skin and no legs that hatches from an egg is probably

(A) a snake

B a worm

C an eel

D a lizard

EXAMPLE: LEVEL 200

Grade 4: 81% Correct Overall

Percent Correct for Anchor Levels
200	250	300	350
72	90	95	—

 Domestic Cat   Dog

Look at the drawing of the cat and dog tracks above. Which of the tracks below was made by an animal in the cat family?

A

B

C

 D

33

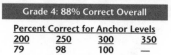

Grade 4: 88% Correct Overall

Percent Correct for Anchor Levels

200	250	300	350
79	98	100	—

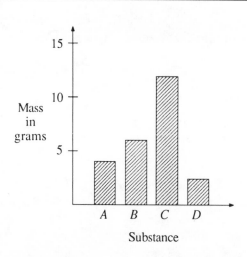

On the basis of the information in the graph above, which of the following substances has the greatest mass?

A *A*

B *B*

Ⓒ *C*

D *D*

LEVEL 250 — APPLIES GENERAL SCIENTIFIC INFORMATION   Students performing at or above Level 250 were typically able to demonstrate knowledge of some basic information in the physical sciences, such as predicting the direction of movement of a rock being pulled in two directions and explaining why stars appear to be smaller than the moon. These students also showed some understanding of basic ecology, as seen in their ability to identify a food chain, and some ability to apply their knowledge of the physical and chemical characteristics of sugar to interpret data in a simple table. A beginning understanding of experimental design also was evidenced by these students, as illustrated by the "water evaporation" item.

EXAMPLE: LEVEL 250

As shown below, two children are moving a heavy rock by pulling with equal force on two ropes attached to it. Assume the ground is smooth and level. Draw an arrow to show the direction that the rock will slide along the ground.

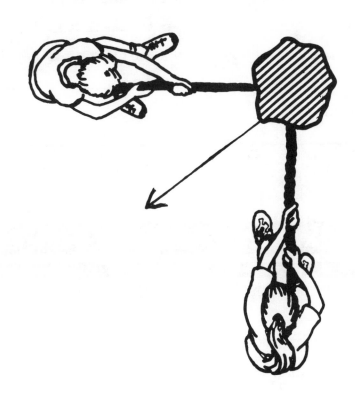

EXAMPLE: LEVEL 250

Stars are bigger than the Moon, but they appear to be smaller when you look at them. Why? Write your answer in your answer book.

Because the moon is closer to earth and stars are farther away. Therefore the moon looks bigger than the stars.

EXAMPLE: LEVEL 250

Juan thinks that water will evaporate faster in a warm place than in a cool one. He has two identical bowls and a bucket of water. He wants to do an experiment to find out if he is correct. Which of the following should he do?

A Place two bowls with the same amount of water in a warm place.

B Place a bowl of water in a cool place and a bowl with twice the amount of water in a warm place.

C Place a bowl of water in a cool place and a bowl with half of the amount of water in a warm place.

D Place a bowl of water in a cool place and a bowl with the same amount of water in a warm place.

EXAMPLE: LEVEL 250

Grade 4: 51% Correct Overall				Grade 8: 78% Correct Overall			
Percent Correct for Anchor Levels				**Percent Correct for Anchor Levels**			
200	250	300	350	200	250	300	350
35	66	93	—	53	80	92	98

Which of the groups of animals pictured below forms a food chain?

A

B

Ⓒ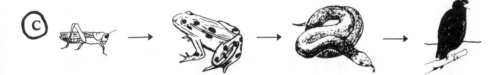

D

EXAMPLE: LEVEL 250

Property	Substance A	Substance B	Substance C	Substance D
State	Solid	Solid	Solid	Liquid
Attracted to Magnet?	Yes	No	No	Yes
Dissolves in Water?	No	No	Yes	No
Color	Black	White	White	Silver

Look at the chart above. Which of the substances shown above could be sugar?

A *A*

B *B*

 C *C*

D *D*

LEVEL 300 — ANALYZES SCIENTIFIC PROCEDURES

AND DATA   The set of example items for Level 300 shows that students performing at or above this level were gaining a somewhat more advanced understanding of principles from the physical sciences, as evidenced by the "light energy," "candle in a box," and "greenhouse effect" questions, and the item which required students to draw the position of the moon during a solar eclipse. These students also appeared to have a more in-depth understanding of basic ecological principles, as demonstrated by their ability to graphically depict the change in the size of a prey population after the extinction of the predator population. A high percentage of students performing at or above Level 300 successfully interpreted information in somewhat detailed graphs, as shown by the "moths and light" item, and were able to design simple experiments, such as those in the "antacid seltzer" and "sugar cubes" items. These students also appeared to be developing an understanding of the nature of science, as shown by their performance on the items asking them to identify which in a series of questions could be answered most easily with an experiment, and to recognize how scientists deal with conflicting hypotheses.

38

EXAMPLE: LEVEL 300

Grade 8: 56% Correct Overall			

Percent Correct for Anchor Levels			
200	**250**	**300**	**350**
33	45	82	93

Grade 12: 72% Correct Overall			

Percent Correct for Anchor Levels			
200	**250**	**300**	**350**
34	47	82	94

Which of the following provides the best evidence that light is a form of energy?

A Light reflects from a smooth surface like glass.

(B) Light raises the temperature of an object on which it falls.

C Light usually travels in straight lines.

D Light diffracts when it passes through a narrow opening.

EXAMPLE: LEVEL 300

Grade 12: 58% Correct Overall			

Percent Correct for Anchor Levels			
200	**250**	**300**	**350**
22	35	65	91

Which of the following may lead to an increase in the greenhouse effect?

(A) An increase in atmospheric concentration of carbon dioxide from increased burning of fossil fuels

B A decrease in the amount of atmospheric dust from volcanic activity

C An increase in solar flares on the Sun's surface

D An increase in variation of Earth's orbit around the Sun

EXAMPLE: LEVEL 300

Airtight Box

Open Box   Airtight Box

Volume =   Volume =   Volume =
400 Cubic Centimeters   400 Cubic Centimeters   1,000 Cubic Centimeters
Box X   Box Y   Box Z

The three identical candles shown above are lit at the same time. In which order will they probably go out?

A X, then Y, and then Z

B Y, then Z, and then X

C Z, then X, and then Y

D Z, then Y, and then X

EXAMPLE: LEVEL 300

Below is a diagram of our Sun and Earth. Where will the Moon be during a solar eclipse as seen from the Earth? Draw the Moon on the dotted line in that position.

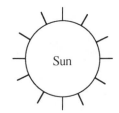

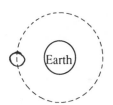

EXAMPLE: LEVEL 300

Cleo wants to conduct an experiment to find out whether an antacid seltzer fizzes longer in hot water than in cold water. In what order should she perform the following steps?

1. Place one antacid seltzer tablet in each jar.
2. Pick identical jars.
3. Time how long the antacid seltzer tablet fizzes in each jar.
4. Pour 50 milliliters (mL) of hot water into one jar and 50 mL of ice water into another jar.

A 1, 2, 3, 4

B 2, 1, 3, 4

C 2, 4, 1, 3

D 3, 2, 4, 1

EXAMPLE: LEVEL 300

The graph below shows how the populations of two species change with time. Species 1 has no predators other than Species 2. Complete the Species 1 line to show how the population will change from time X to time Y after Species 2 dies off from a widespread disease.

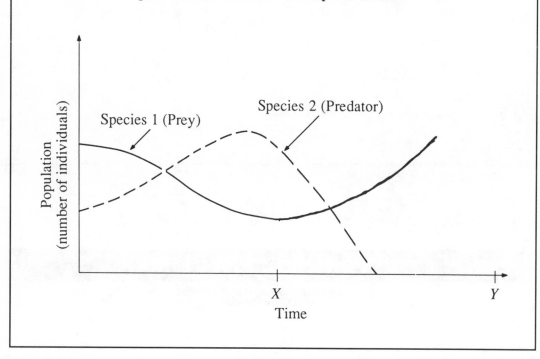

42

EXAMPLE: LEVEL 300

▶ **Questions 8–9** refer to an experiment in which moths were captured by attracting them to either white or yellow light. The results are shown in the graph below.

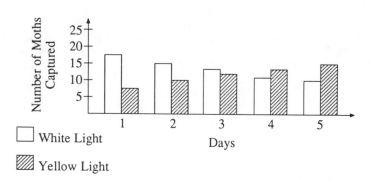

The average number of moths caught per day in yellow light is about

A 5

B 12

C 20

D 28

43

EXAMPLE: LEVEL 300

Grade 4: 21% Correct Overall				Grade 8: 53% Correct Overall			
Percent Correct for Anchor Levels				**Percent Correct for Anchor Levels**			
200	**250**	**300**	**350**	**200**	**250**	**300**	**350**
4	27	75	—	16	48	79	96

Sugar Cubes   Loose Sugar

Two forms of sugar are shown above—solid cubes and packets of loose crystals. One cube has the same amount of sugar as one packet. Write your answers to the following questions in your **ANSWER BOOK.**

Describe what you would do to find out which form dissolves faster, using the following materials: 2 identical drinking glasses, a stopwatch, spoons, a measuring cup, and water.

First I would measure the same Amount of water and put both in 2. identical drinking glasses. Then at the same, drop the loose sugar packet in one glass and a sugar cube in the other with the spoon—I would mix the water and with the stopwatch time the time it takes for each to dissolve.

44

EXAMPLE: LEVEL 300

Grade 4: 33% Correct Overall			
Percent Correct for Anchor Levels			
200	250	300	350
25	36	75	—

Grade 8: 57% Correct Overall			
Percent Correct for Anchor Levels			
200	250	300	350
35	50	81	94

Which of the following questions would be the easiest to answer with an experiment?

A How many uses are there for magnets?

(B) Which is the stronger of two magnets?

C What makes a magnet strong?

D How are magnets made?

EXAMPLE: LEVEL 300

Grade 12: 62% Correct Overall			
Percent Correct for Anchor Levels			
200	250	300	350
12	41	73	92

A scientist develops a theory to explain some phenomena that previous theories could not. However, this theory leads to predictions that are contrary to other scientists' expectations. What should be done in response to these results?

A Ignore the expectations and accept the theory.

B Reject the theory since it is contrary to the expectations.

C Revise the theory so that it agrees with the expectations.

(D) Design experiments to test for the predictions made by the theory.

E Develop another theory that predicts what the scientists expected.

LEVEL 350 — INTEGRATES
SPECIALIZED SCIENTIFIC
INFORMATION   An examination of the set of example items illustrating performance at Level 350 reveals that a high percentage of students performing at or above this level had developed a somewhat advanced understanding of experimental design and could use somewhat more detailed knowledge from life, physical, and earth sciences to help them draw conclusions and infer relationships from data in figures and tables. For example, students performing at Level 350 were more likely than those at Level 300 to draw valid conclusions from a figure containing results from an experiment with two variables (temperature and germination/nongermination) and successfully predict the type of fossil that would be found in a particular rock layer, given information about fossils in adjacent rock layers.

EXAMPLE: LEVEL 350

Percent Correct for Anchor Levels				Percent Correct for Anchor Levels			
200	250	300	350	200	250	300	350
26	22	37	66	22	17	40	70

Jamal has twenty silk worm larvae. Half are 2 centimeters long and half are 4 centimeters long. He knows the length of time it takes the smaller larvae to consume 100 grams of mulberry leaves. Which of the following information should he collect for the 4-centimeter larvae in order to compare the eating rates of the two sets of larvae?

A Time for all ten larvae to eat 100 grams of leaves

B Time for each larva to eat one leaf

C Weight of leaves eaten by all ten larvae in an hour

D Number of leaves eaten by all ten larvae in a day

47

EXAMPLE: LEVEL 350

Grade 8: 25% Correct Overall					Grade 12: 38% Correct Overall			

Percent Correct for Anchor Levels					Percent Correct for Anchor Levels			
200	**250**	**300**	**350**		**200**	**250**	**300**	**350**
16	19	36	69		14	21	36	72

 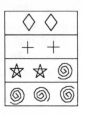 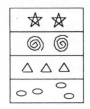

Northern U.S.   Southwest U.S.   Northern Europe

If the diagrams above represent rock layers at three different places on Earth and the shapes in the diagrams represent the type of fossils found in each rock layer, which of the following is most likely to be found immediately below the lowest rock layer in the Southwest U.S.?

A ◇

B ○

C ☆

 △

48

EXAMPLE: LEVEL 350

Percent Correct for Anchor Levels			
200	250	300	350
5	19	42	73

An antacid seltzer tablet is dropped into each of two glasses containing equal amounts of water. The temperature of the water is 50°C in Glass 1 and 10°C in Glass 2. In each glass, bubbles of gas are released as the tablet dissolves. It takes 30 seconds for the tablet to react completely in Glass 1 and 100 seconds for the tablet to react completely in Glass 2. From these results alone, one can conclude that

A temperature has no effect on the rate of chemical reactions

B increasing the volume of water increases the rate at which the antacid seltzer reacts with water

C the rate of all chemical reactions increases as the temperature increases

D the rate of chemical reactions doubles for every 10°C increases in temperature

E the rate at which the antacid seltzer reacts with water is faster in hot water than in cold water

EXAMPLE: LEVEL 350

Percent Correct for Anchor Levels			
200	250	300	350
31	33	48	86

Percent Correct for Anchor Levels			
200	250	300	350
37	34	50	89

Which of the following methods could be used to find out how much space is taken up by rocks placed in a 1-liter container?

A Weigh the rocks, and then weigh the container, then subtract the weight of the container from the rocks.

B Empty the container and count the number of rocks.

C Fill the container holding the rocks with water, pour the water into a measuring cup, then subtract the amount of water from the entire capacity of the container.

D Weigh the container empty, fill it with the rocks and water, then weigh it again.

▶ **Questions 17–18** refer to an experiment that is set up to determine the volume of O_2 consumed by germinating and nongerminating (dry) peas, each at two different temperatures. The data are shown below.

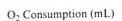
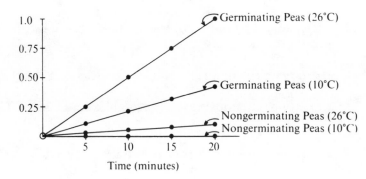

Which of the following conclusions is best supported by the data?

A Nongerminating peas have a higher rate of respiration than do germinating peas.

B Light is required for pea seed germination.

C In nongerminating peas, oxygen consumption is directly proportional to oxygen concentration.

D Less carbon dioxide is produced by germinating pea seeds at 26°C than at 10°C.

E In germinating peas, an increase in temperature results in an increase in oxygen consumption.

50

LEVELS OF SCIENCE PROFICIENCY

BY GENDER   TABLE 2.1 summarizes the results by gender for students performing at or above each of the four proficiency levels.

TABLE 2.1
Percentages of Students at or above Four Proficiency Levels on the NAEP Science Scale by Gender

| | PERCENT OF STUDENTS AT OR ABOVE | | | |
	Level 200	Level 250	Level 300	Level 350
GRADE 4				
Male	85 (1.0)	32 (1.7)	1 (0.2)	0 (0.0)
Female	84 (1.0)	29 (1.6)	1 (0.3)	0 (0.0)
GRADE 8				
Male	94 (0.8)	65 (1.6)	21 (1.5)	1 (0.4)
Female	94 (0.8)	63 (1.5)	15 (1.2)	0 (0.1)
GRADE 12				
Male	99 (0.3)	86 (1.0)	49 (1.4)	13 (1.1)
Female	98 (0.3)	83 (1.1)	40 (1.3)	6 (0.7)

The standard errors of the estimated percentages appear in parentheses. It can be said with 95 percent certainty that for each population of interest, the value for the whole population is within plus or minus two standard errors of the estimate for the sample. When the percentage of students is either 0 or 100, the standard error is inestimable. However, percentages 99.5 percent and greater were rounded to 100 percent and percentages less than 0.5 percent were rounded to 0 percent.

The 1990 Science Report Card: NAEP's Assessment of Fourth, Eighth, and Twelfth Graders (National Center for Education Statistics, U.S. Department of Education, 1992).

At grade 4, the results for both males and females paralleled those for the nation as a whole and there were no significant differences in the percentages of male and female fourth graders performing at or above any of the proficiency levels. At grade 8, a significantly higher percentage of males than females performed at or above Level 300 (21 compared to 15 percent). At grade 12, the gender gap was more pervasive, with statistically significant differences favoring males at Levels 250, 300, and 350. Among the high school seniors, 49 percent of the males performed at or above Level 300 and 13 percent reached Level 350, as compared to 40 percent and 6 percent of the females, respectively. These results support other recent evidence showing that gender differences in achievement in science increase between the elementary grades and high school, and highlight the continuing need for efforts to improve the opportunities for female high school students to learn science.[12]

[12] Marlaine E. Lockheed, et al., *Sex and Ethnic Differences: Middle School Mathematics, Science, and Computer Science: What Do We Know?* (Princeton, NJ: Educational Testing Service, 1985).
The High Stakes of High School Science (Washington, D.C.: The National Center for Improving Science Education, 1991).

The percentage of students who performed at or above each of the four proficiency levels by race/ethnicity are presented in TABLE 2.2. Large disparities in the percentages of students from different racial/ethnic subpopulations are present for at least two of the proficiency levels in each of the three grades.

TABLE 2.2
Percentages of Students at or above Four Proficiency Levels on the NAEP Science Scale by Race/Ethnicity

	PERCENT OF STUDENTS AT OR ABOVE			
	Level 200	Level 250	Level 300	Level 350
GRADE 4				
White	93 (0.8)	40 (1.6)	1 (0.3)	0 (0.0)
Black	58 (2.7)	5 (1.1)	0 (0.2)	0 (0.0)
Hispanic	66 (2.4)	10 (1.2)	0 (0.0)	0 (0.0)
Asian/Pacific Islander	88 (3.1)	29 (5.2)	2 (1.5)	0 (0.0)
American Indian	81 (5.3)	20 (4.8)	0 (0.0)	0 (0.0)
GRADE 8				
White	97 (0.5)	74 (1.3)	23 (1.3)	1 (0.3)
Black	80 (2.5)	31 (2.5)	3 (0.8)	0 (0.1)
Hispanic	87 (1.7)	42 (2.8)	5 (0.9)	0 (0.1)
Asian/Pacific Islander	96 (1.9)	71 (4.8)	23 (4.1)	1 (0.6)
American Indian	92 (2.8)!	54 (11.6)!	8 (2.8)!	0 (0.0)!
GRADE 12				
White	100 (0.1)	91 (0.8)	53 (1.4)	12 (0.9)
Black	94 (1.4)	57 (3.0)	12 (2.0)	1 (0.6)
Hispanic	98 (0.8)	70 (3.4)	23 (2.9)	3 (1.0)
Asian/Pacific Islander	99 (1.4)	90 (3.2)	60 (7.4)	17 (5.0)
American Indian	100 (0.7)!	89 (5.6)!	33 (9.3)!	2 (0.0)!

The standard errors of the estimated percentages appear in parentheses. It can be said with 95 percent certainty that for each population of interest, the value for the whole population is within plus or minus two standard errors of the estimate for the sample. When the percentage of students is either 0 or 100, the standard error is inestimable. However, percentages 99.5 percent and greater were rounded to 100 percent and percentages less than 0.5 percent were rounded to 0 percent.

! Interpret with caution — the nature of the sample does not allow accurate determination of the variability of these estimated statistics.

The 1990 Science Report Card: NAEP's Assessment of Fourth, Eighth, and Twelfth Graders (National Center for Education Statistics, U.S. Department of Education, 1992).

At grade 4, significantly higher percentages of White and Asian/Pacific Islander students reached Level 200 and 250 than did their Black and Hispanic counterparts. The results for Level 250 are particularly striking. Forty percent of White and about 30 percent of Asian/Pacific Islander fourth graders performed at or above this level, as compared to 10 percent of Hispanic and 5 percent of Black fourth graders. These data further support the results presented in Chapter One showing that, on average, substantial differences in science achievement exist by the fourth grade between White students and their Black and Hispanic counterparts.

Similar differences can also be observed in the data for the eighth and twelfth grades. At grade 8, higher percentages of White and Asian/Pacific Islander students achieved at or above Levels 200, 250, and 300 than did Black or Hispanic students and at grade 12, these differences occurred at Levels 250, 300, and 350. It is especially worth noting that while more than half of White and Asian/Pacific Islander twelfth-grade students reached Level 300 or above, only 23 percent of Hispanic students and 12 percent of Black students did so.

The percentages of American Indian students who performed at or above each of the four proficiency levels generally fell between the percentages of White students and the percentages of Black students. However, because the size of the sample of American Indian students was relatively small and the science proficiency for this subpopulation was somewhat variable, only a few of the apparent differences between the percentages of American Indian students and students in the other four racial/ethnic groups were statistically significant. Significantly higher percentages of American Indian students than Black students performed at or above Level 200 at each of the three grades and at or above Level 250 at grades 4 and 12. A significantly lower percentage of American Indian students than White students performed at or above Level 250 at grade 4 and at or above Level 300 at grade 8.

LEVELS OF SCIENCE PROFICIENCY

BY REGION   Regional results for students performing at or above each of the four proficiency levels are displayed in TABLE 2.3.

In general, at grades 4 and 8, the percentages of students at or above each of the four proficiency levels paralleled the results for the nation as a whole. A higher percentage of fourth graders in the Northeast achieved at or above Level 250 than in the Southeast and higher percentages of eighth graders in the Northeast and Central regions achieved at or above Levels 250 and 300 than did their counterparts in the Southeast.

TABLE 2.3
Percentages of Students at or above Four Proficiency Levels on the NAEP Science Scale by Region

	PERCENT OF STUDENTS AT OR ABOVE			
	Level 200	**Level 250**	**Level 300**	**Level 350**
GRADE 4				
Northeast	86 (1.8)	36 (3.0)	1 (0.7)	0 (0.0)
Southeast	80 (2.5)	23 (2.5)	1 (0.2)	0 (0.0)
Central	87 (2.0)	31 (3.1)	1 (0.3)	0 (0.0)
West	85 (1.7)	33 (2.8)	1 (0.3)	0 (0.0)
GRADE 8				
Northeast	95 (1.5)	71 (2.9)	22 (2.0)	1 (0.4)
Southeast	92 (1.5)	58 (2.0)	13 (1.3)	1 (0.3)
Central	94 (1.2)	67 (2.6)	18 (1.4)	0 (0.4)
West	94 (1.2)	63 (2.5)	19 (2.9)	1 (0.4)
GRADE 12				
Northeast	99 (0.5)	87 (2.4)	52 (2.9)	12 (2.0)
Southeast	98 (0.6)	75 (2.4)	31 (2.5)	4 (0.8)
Central	99 (0.5)	86 (1.4)	47 (2.0)	9 (1.5)
West	99 (0.4)	86 (1.8)	46 (2.6)	12 (1.7)

The standard errors of the estimated percentages appear in parentheses. It can be said with 95 percent certainty that for each population of interest, the value for the whole population is within plus or minus two standard errors of the estimate for the sample. When the percentage of students is either 0 or 100, the standard error is inestimable. However, percentages 99.5 percent and greater were rounded to 100 percent and percentages less than 0.5 percent were rounded to 0 percent.

The 1990 Science Report Card: NAEP's Assessment of Fourth, Eighth, and Twelfth Graders (National Center for Education Statistics, U.S. Department of Education, 1992).

At grade 12, the disparity between students in the Southeast and the other three regions occurred more consistently. The percentages of twelfth-grade students from the Northeast, Central, and West regions performing at or above Levels 250, 300, and 350 were significantly higher than the percentages of twelfth graders in the Southeast who performed at or above these three proficiency levels.

LEVELS OF SCIENCE PROFICIENCY BY TYPE OF COMMUNITY   To provide some information relevant to socioeconomic level, NAEP analyzed results for students attending schools in three extreme types of communities — advantaged urban, disadvantaged urban, and extreme rural — as compared to students in the remaining types of communities. The results by type of community are shown in TABLE 2.4.

TABLE 2.4

Percentages of Students at or above Four Proficiency Levels on the NAEP Science Scale by Type of Community

	PERCENT OF STUDENTS AT OR ABOVE			
	Level 200	Level 250	Level 300	Level 350
GRADE 4				
Advantaged Urban	96 (1.5)	55 (3.9)	3 (0.9)	0 (0.0)
Disadvantaged Urban	59 (3.9)	10 (2.0)	0 (0.0)	0 (0.0)
Extreme Rural	89 (2.7)	30 (3.5)	0 (0.4)	0 (0.0)
Other	85 (1.1)	30 (1.4)	1 (0.2)	0 (0.0)
GRADE 8				
Advantaged Urban	99 (0.6)!	82 (2.6)!	34 (5.4)!	2 (1.0)!
Disadvantaged Urban	84 (3.2)	43 (3.8)	8 (1.7)	0 (0.2)
Extreme Rural	93 (1.7)	58 (4.1)	13 (2.4)	0 (0.3)
Other	94 (0.8)	65 (1.5)	18 (1.1)	1 (0.3)
GRADE 12				
Advantaged Urban	99 (0.9)!	87 (2.8)!	57 (4.4)!	14 (2.2)!
Disadvantaged Urban	96 (1.8)	69 (5.0)	27 (3.7)	4 (1.0)
Extreme Rural	99 (0.6)!	85 (3.0)!	41 (3.8)!	7 (1.7)!
Other	99 (0.2)	86 (1.1)	47 (1.5)	10 (1.1)

The standard errors of the estimated percentages appear in parentheses. It can be said with 95 percent certainty that for each population of interest, the value for the whole population is within plus or minus two standard errors of the estimate for the sample. When the percentage of students is either 0 or 100, the standard error is inestimable. However, percentages 99.5 percent and greater were rounded to 100 percent and percentages less than 0.5 percent were rounded to 0 percent.

! Interpret with caution — the nature of the sample does not allow accurate determination of the variability of these estimated statistics.

The 1990 Science Report Card: NAEP's Assessment of Fourth, Eighth, and Twelfth Graders (National Center for Education Statistics, U.S. Department of Education, 1992).

These results reveal large discrepancies between the science achievement of students in disadvantaged urban communities and that of their grade-level counterparts in each of the other community types. At grades 4 and 8, the percentages of students in disadvantaged urban communities who performed at or above Levels 200 and 250 were lower than the percentages of students from advantaged urban communities, extreme rural communities, and communities classified as "other" who performed at these levels. These differences also existed at Levels 250 and 300 at grade 12. In addition, higher percentages of students from advantaged urban and "other" community types achieved at or above Level 300 at grade 8 and Level 350 at grade 12 than did students from disadvantaged urban communities. Taken as a whole, these results indicate that relatively high percentages of students from disadvantaged urban communities have difficulty understanding and applying basic scientific principles or performing the more advanced evaluative and integrative activities expected of students who might pursue further coursework in science.

In each of the three grades, the percentages of students from extreme rural communities who performed at or above the four proficiency levels did not differ significantly from the percentages of students from communities classified as "other" who performed at or above these same levels. However, when compared with results for students from advantaged urban communities, lower percentages of students from extreme rural communities performed at or above Level 250 at grade 4; Levels 200, 250, and 300 at grade 8; and Levels 300 and 350 at grade 12.

LEVELS OF SCIENCE PROFICIENCY BY TYPE OF SCHOOL

TABLE 2.5 presents the percentages of public and private school students performing at or above each level of proficiency. Private school students include students attending Catholic schools and students attending other types of private schools.

TABLE 2.5
Percentages of Students at or above Four Proficiency Levels on the NAEP Science Scale by Type of School

	PERCENT OF STUDENTS AT OR ABOVE			
	Level 200	Level 250	Level 300	Level 350
GRADE 4				
Public Schools	83 (1.0)	29 (1.4)	1 (0.2)	0 (0.0)
Private Schools	94 (1.2)	42 (3.1)	2 (0.4)	0 (0.0)
GRADE 8				
Public Schools	93 (0.7)	63 (1.3)	17 (1.1)	1 (0.2)
Private Schools	98 (0.8)	76 (2.3)	23 (1.7)	1 (0.5)
GRADE 12				
Public Schools	99 (0.2)	83 (0.9)	44 (1.3)	9 (0.8)
Private Schools	100 (0.2)	91 (1.5)	52 (2.7)	10 (1.7)

The standard errors of the estimated percentages appear in parentheses. It can be said with 95 percent certainty that for each population of interest, the value for the whole population is within plus or minus two standard errors of the estimate for the sample. When the percentage of students is either 0 or 100, the standard error is inestimable. However, percentages 99.5 percent and greater were rounded to 100 percent and percentages less than 0.5 percent were rounded to 0 percent.

The 1990 Science Report Card: NAEP's Assessment of Fourth, Eighth, and Twelfth Graders (National Center for Education Statistics, U.S. Department of Education, 1992).

In each of the three grades, because most students attend public schools, the percentages of public school students achieving at or above each proficiency level generally paralleled the percentages for the national sample. However, the percentages of private school students were higher than the percentages of public school students for a number of the levels at each grade — at Levels 200 and 250 at grade 4; at Levels 200, 250, and 300 at grade 8; and at Levels 250 and 300 at grade 12.

LEVELS OF SCIENCE PROFICIENCY BY PARENTS' HIGHEST LEVEL OF EDUCATION Percentages of students achieving at or above the four proficiency levels by parents' highest level of education are shown in TABLE 2.6.

TABLE 2.6
Percentages of Students at or above Four Proficiency Levels on the NAEP Science Scale by Parents' Highest Level of Education

	PERCENT OF STUDENTS AT OR ABOVE			
	Level 200	**Level 250**	**Level 300**	**Level 350**
GRADE 4				
Did Not Finish HS	78 (3.7)	16 (4.2)	0 (0.0)	0 (0.0)
Graduated From HS	81 (1.8)	21 (2.0)	0 (0.3)	0 (0.0)
Some Education After HS	91 (1.4)	42 (2.9)	1 (0.8)	0 (0.0)
Graduated From College	90 (0.9)	44 (1.9)	2 (0.3)	0 (0.0)
GRADE 8				
Did Not Finish HS	89 (2.9)	41 (3.0)	4 (1.2)	0 (0.0)
Graduated From HS	92 (1.0)	56 (1.8)	10 (0.9)	0 (0.2)
Some Education After HS	96 (0.7)	72 (1.9)	19 (1.7)	1 (0.4)
Graduated From College	97 (0.5)	76 (1.5)	29 (2.0)	1 (0.3)
GRADE 12				
Did Not Finish HS	98 (0.7)	68 (3.3)	21 (2.8)	2 (1.0)
Graduated From HS	98 (0.6)	77 (1.6)	30 (1.4)	3 (0.7)
Some Education After HS	99 (0.2)	88 (1.3)	45 (1.7)	8 (1.0)
Graduated From College	99 (0.2)	91 (0.7)	59 (1.6)	16 (1.5)

The standard errors of the estimated percentages appear in parentheses. It can be said with 95 percent certainty that for each population of interest, the value for the whole population is within plus or minus two standard errors of the estimate for the sample. When the percentage of students is either 0 or 100, the standard error is inestimable. However, percentages 99.5 percent and greater were rounded to 100 percent and percentages less than 0.5 percent were rounded to 0 percent.

The 1990 Science Report Card: NAEP's Assessment of Fourth, Eighth, and Twelfth Graders (National Center for Education Statistics, U.S. Department of Education, 1992).

In general, for students in all three grades, those with parents with progressively more education tended to achieve progressively better on the science assessment. At grade 4, the percentages of students at or above Levels 200 and 250 whose parents had not graduated from high school or had graduated from high school (but had no further education) were lower than the percentages of students who had at least one parent who had some education beyond high school or had graduated from college. Similar relationships between parents' level of education and the percentages of students at or above Levels 200, 250, and 300 occurred at grade 8 and at Levels 250, 300, and 350 at grade 12. For example, 59 percent of the twelfth graders who had at least one parent who had graduated from college performed at or above Level 300 compared to 45 percent whose parents had only some post-secondary education, 30 percent whose parents had graduated from high school, and 21 percent whose parents had not graduated from high school.

SUMMARY   Results from NAEP's 1990 science assessment presented for a range of four levels of proficiency support the overall achievement results presented in Chapter One, and show that only small percentages of students in any of the three grades consistently demonstrated the abilities characteristic of performance at the highest two proficiency levels. Even for high school seniors about to enter the work force or pursue post-secondary education and training, fewer than one-half performed at or above Level 300, which was typified by the ability to apply knowledge to interpret tables and graphs, evaluate and design experiments, and demonstrate some detailed knowledge of scientific information. In addition, at all three grades, the percentages of White and Asian/Pacific Islander students performing at or above the highest levels generally reached by students in each grade were significantly larger than the corresponding percentages of Hispanic and Black students. Also, within each of the three grades, substantially larger percentages of students from advantaged urban communities attained higher levels than did their counterparts from disadvantaged urban communities. No differences in the percentages of male and female students existed at any level of proficiency at grade 4; however, a slightly greater percentage of males than females performed at or above Level 300 at grade 8. This gender difference occurred at Levels 250, 300, and 350 at grade 12, indicating that gender differences in science achievement, particularly at the highest levels of proficiency, increase as students progress through school.

Few differences in the percentages of students performing at or above the four proficiency levels occurred by region. However, at grade 12, smaller percentages of students from the Southeast performed at or above Levels 250, 300, and 350 than did students in the other three regions. Higher percentages of private school students performed at or above two or more proficiency levels at all three grades, as compared to their public school counterparts. In general, for students in all three grades, the higher the level of parental education, the higher the percentages of students performing at or above each of the highest three proficiency levels.

In their 1983 report to the American people, *Educating Americans for the 21st Century,* the National Science Board Commission presented a plan of action for improving mathematics and science education for secondary students so that their achievement would be the best in the world by 1995.[13] These recommendations included providing opportunity and high standards of excellence for all students — wherever they lived, whatever their race, gender, or economic condition. Today, as we face a revised national goal of having U.S. students first in the world in science and mathematics achievement by the year 2000, the NAEP data presented in Chapters One and Two indicate that the earlier call for universal opportunities and excellence in science education is just as pertinent nearly a decade later as it was in 1983.

[13] *Educating Americans for the 21st Century: A Report to the American People and the National Science Board* (Washington, D.C.: National Science Board Commission on Precollege Education in Mathematics, Science, and Technology, 1983).

SCIENCE PROFICIENCY BY CONTENT AREAS FOR THE NATION, SUBPOPULATIONS, AND IN RELATION TO HIGH SCHOOL COURSE-TAKING

What is the proficiency of students in the various disciplines of science? How much science course work do students take during high school? This chapter presents information about students' proficiency in particular science content areas and, for high-school seniors, the relationship between course-taking in those particular content areas and proficiency. Although the disciplines of science are interconnected in many ways, in order to parallel the present curriculum, the framework underlying NAEP's 1990 science assessment reflected three traditional disciplines of science: life sciences, physical sciences, and earth and space sciences.[14] In addition, an

---

[14] *Science Objectives, 1990 Assessment* (Princeton, NJ: National Assessment of Educational Progress, Educational Testing Service, 1989.)

awareness and understanding of the nature of science — that is, a recognition of science as a way of knowing — served as a foundation for the framework. Results are presented for the three traditional content areas and for the nature of science content area, each of which is briefly described in FIGURE 3.1.

FIGURE 3.1
Description of Science Content Areas

LIFE SCIENCES

Concepts in the life sciences can be placed along a continuum, ranging from the topic-specific to the highly integrated and interdisciplinary. Most students gain some topic-specific knowledge and understandings in this content area through life experiences; thus, some topic-specific questions, such as asking students to classify plants and animals, are most appropriate at the earlier grade levels. In contrast, items for older students — for example, questions dealing with energy transformations or genetics — require integration of knowledge from several disciplines, as these students are assumed to have mastered a detailed knowledge of the simpler (i.e., topic-specific) categories. The major categories of topics in the life sciences included in the 1990 assessment include cellular and molecular biology, energy transformations, genetic continuity and development, evolution, diversity and systematics, structure and function of organisms, behavior, and ecology.

PHYSICAL SCIENCES

The physical sciences deal with the fundamental components of the natural universe — space, time, matter, and energy. Students should understand the properties of matter and how the elements are organized in the periodic table. Students should also understand that the universe is not static; rather, matter and energy are continually being transformed in space and time, producing chemical and physical changes. A grasp of the laws of mechanics, and the interaction of light and matter, provides a way of understanding that among all of nature's transformations, a few invariable (conserved) quantities are known to exist, including mass-energy, electrical charge, and linear and angular momentum. In addition, an understanding of energy — more specifically, the laws of thermodynamics — permits one to predict if and in what manner a change will occur. The six sets of topics included in the 1990 science assessment are motion, conserved quantities, waves, particulate nature of matter, properties of matter, and changes.

EARTH AND SPACE SCIENCES

Knowledge and understanding of key concepts in the earth and space sciences provides students with a more informed view of their place on Earth, and of Earth's place within the universe. These concepts, in turn, build students' capacity to participate in public decisions, particularly those concerning environmental issues. Earth's place within the universe, plate tectonics, water and rock cycles, and the Earth's history constitute the earth and space science topics included in the 1990 assessment.

THE NATURE OF SCIENCE

Three aspects of the nature of science were included in the 1990 assessment — processes, principles, and knowledge. The processes of science encompass observing, classifying, and inferring; interpreting data; formulating hypotheses; designing experiments; and conducting inquiries. The nature of values and principles underlying scientific work include: knowledge is valued, questioning is essential, data are fundamental, verification is essential, and logic is respected. The nature of scientific knowledge was defined according to five major tenets: scientific knowledge is 1) tentative, 2) public, 3) empirically based, 4) based on replicable observations, and 5) cumulative.

AVERAGE PROFICIENCY IN SCIENCE

BY CONTENT AREAS   The average proficiency results for the four content areas are presented in FIGURE 3.2, which summarizes student performance at grades 4, 8, and 12 for each content area. As expected, average proficiency at grade 12 exceeded that at grade 8, and average proficiency at grade 8 exceeded that at grade 4 in each of the content areas. Within each of the content areas, with the exception of the nature of science, the difference in performance between grades 4 and 8 was generally comparable to the difference between grades 8 and 12.

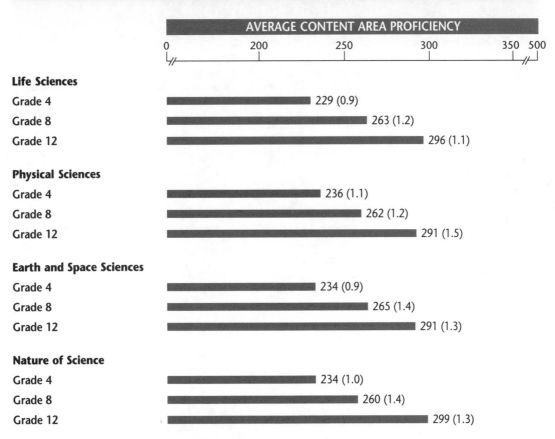

FIGURE 3.2
Average Proficiency in Science
Content Areas for the Nation

AVERAGE CONTENT AREA PROFICIENCY

Life Sciences

Grade 4	229 (0.9)
Grade 8	263 (1.2)
Grade 12	296 (1.1)

Physical Sciences

Grade 4	236 (1.1)
Grade 8	262 (1.2)
Grade 12	291 (1.5)

Earth and Space Sciences

Grade 4	234 (0.9)
Grade 8	265 (1.4)
Grade 12	291 (1.3)

Nature of Science

Grade 4	234 (1.0)
Grade 8	260 (1.4)
Grade 12	299 (1.3)

The standard errors of the estimated proficiencies appear in parentheses. It can be said with 95 percent certainty that for each population of interest, the value for the whole population is within plus or minus two standard errors of the estimate for the sample.

The 1990 Science Report Card: NAEP's Assessment of Fourth, Eighth, and Twelfth Graders (National Center for Education Statistics, U.S. Department of Education, 1992).

AVERAGE PROFICIENCY IN

SCIENCE CONTENT AREAS

BY RACE/ETHNICITY   Average proficiency in the four content areas for
White, Black, Hispanic, Asian/Pacific Islander, and American Indian students is shown in
TABLE 3.1. At grade 4, in all four content areas, White students had higher average proficiency than students in other racial/ethnic groups, with the exception of Asian/Pacific
Islander students. Also, Asian/Pacific Islander and American Indian students outperformed
their Black and Hispanic counterparts. Hispanic fourth graders had higher average proficiency than fourth-grade Black students in the area of earth and space sciences, but the
two groups had similar average proficiency in the remaining three content areas.

TABLE 3.1
Distribution of Students and Average Proficiency in Science Content Areas by Race/Ethnicity

	Percent of Students	Life Sciences	Physical Sciences	Earth and Space Sciences	Nature of Science
GRADE 4					
White	70 (0.5)	238 (1.0)	245 (1.2)	243 (1.1)	242 (1.1)
Black	15 (0.4)	204 (1.6)	207 (2.0)	204 (1.5)	212 (1.7)
Hispanic	11 (0.3)	209 (1.8)	213 (1.6)	215 (1.6)	212 (1.7)
Asian/Pacific Islander	2 (0.3)	227 (4.1)	238 (3.9)	233 (3.6)	238 (3.5)
American Indian	2 (0.3)	222 (3.8)	229 (4.0)	228 (3.6)	226 (3.8)
GRADE 8					
White	71 (0.4)	273 (1.4)	271 (1.4)	276 (1.5)	270 (1.5)
Black	15 (0.4)	233 (2.3)	232 (2.3)	228 (2.6)	230 (2.7)
Hispanic	10 (0.3)	242 (2.4)	241 (2.2)	242 (2.3)	236 (2.4)
Asian/Pacific Islander	3 (0.4)	272 (4.0)	271 (3.9)	270 (4.3)	267 (5.2)
American Indian	1 (0.5)!	252 (9.7)!	250 (7.8)!	257 (7.3)!	244 (15.6)!
GRADE 12					
White	73 (0.4)	305 (1.1)	300 (1.7)	301 (1.3)	307 (1.4)
Black	14 (0.5)	262 (2.0)	253 (3.1)	247 (2.8)	267 (3.0)
Hispanic	8 (0.3)	275 (2.7)	271 (3.2)	270 (2.9)	277 (3.9)
Asian/Pacific Islander	4 (0.2)	309 (7.1)	310 (8.3)	304 (6.6)	312 (6.9)
American Indian	1 (0.2)!	287 (4.5)!	283 (5.6)!	289 (6.1)!	283 (9.6)!

The standard errors of the estimated percentages and proficiencies appear in parentheses. It can be said with 95 percent
certainty that for each population of interest, the value for the whole population is within plus or minus two standard errors
of the estimate for the sample.

! Interpret with caution — the nature of the sample does not allow accurate determination of the variability of these estimated
statistics.

The 1990 Science Report Card: NAEP's Assessment of Fourth, Eighth, and Twelfth Graders (National Center for Education Statistics,
U.S. Department of Education, 1992).

At grade 8, White and Asian/Pacific Islander students had higher average proficiency than did Black and Hispanic students in all four science content areas. In addition, Hispanic and American Indian eighth graders outperformed their Black counterparts in the area of earth and space sciences.

At grade 12, the pattern was similar to that at grade 8. For all four content areas, White and Asian/Pacific Islander twelfth graders had higher average proficiency than did Black and Hispanic twelfth graders. Hispanic and American Indian twelfth graders performed better than their Black counterparts in every content area except the nature of science.

In general, White and Asian/Pacific Islander students tended to have the highest average proficiency across the content areas, but their relative position tended to shift from the lower to the upper grades. Although the differences in performance were not statistically significant, the pattern for all four content areas was one of White students outperforming their Asian/Pacific Islander classmates at grade 4, the differences between the two groups being negligible at grade 8, and the Asian/Pacific Islander students having a slight advantage at grade 12. For the remaining three racial/ethnic subgroups at all three grades across all four content areas, the pattern was one of American Indian students tending to outperform Hispanic students, who, in turn, tended to have higher proficiency than their Black classmates.

AVERAGE PROFICIENCY IN SCIENCE CONTENT AREAS

BY GENDER   As presented in TABLE 3.2, the analysis of student achievement in the science content areas by gender shows several interesting patterns. First, for the three major content areas of life, physical, and earth and space sciences, a male advantage appeared to emerge as students progress through school. At grade 4, males had higher proficiency than did females in the earth and space sciences, but there was no difference in performance between the genders in either the life or physical sciences areas. However, at grade 8, males outperformed females in the physical sciences area as well as the earth and space sciences and at grade 12, they had higher proficiency than did females in all three of these traditional science content areas. In contrast, at all three grades females had higher proficiency than did males in the area covering the nature of science.

TABLE 3.2
Distribution of Students and Average Proficiency in Science Content Areas by Gender

	Percent of Students	Life Sciences	Physical Sciences	Earth and Space Sciences	Nature of Science
GRADE 4					
Male	51 (0.7)	229 (1.2)	237 (1.3)	237 (1.2)	231 (1.1)
Female	49 (0.7)	229 (1.2)	234 (1.1)	230 (1.1)	236 (1.1)
GRADE 8					
Male	50 (0.8)	264 (1.7)	265 (1.6)	270 (1.6)	257 (1.7)
Female	50 (0.8)	263 (1.2)	260 (1.4)	259 (1.5)	264 (1.5)
GRADE 12					
Male	48 (0.8)	299 (1.5)	299 (2.1)	300 (1.5)	296 (1.7)
Female	52 (0.8)	293 (1.1)	284 (1.3)	283 (1.4)	301 (1.5)

The standard errors of the estimated percentages and proficiencies appear in parentheses. It can be said with 95 percent certainty that for each population of interest, the value for the whole population is within plus or minus two standard errors of the estimate for the sample.

The 1990 Science Report Card: NAEP's Assessment of Fourth, Eighth, and Twelfth Graders (National Center for Education Statistics, U.S. Department of Education, 1992).

AVERAGE PROFICIENCY IN SCIENCE CONTENT AREAS

BY REGION   The regional results by science content area are summarized in TABLE 3.3. At grade 4, there were no significant differences across the regions in performance for either the life sciences or nature of science content areas. However, fourth graders in the Southeast did have lower average proficiency in the physical sciences than did students in the other three regions of the country, as well as lower average proficiency in the earth and space sciences area than their counterparts in the Northeast and West. Eighth graders in the Northeast performed better than those in the Southeast in all four science content areas. Also, eighth graders in the Central region had significantly higher proficiency than those in the Southeast in two content areas — life sciences and the nature of science. At grade 12, however, students in the Southeast had lower average proficiency than their counterparts in the other three regions of the country in all four content areas.

TABLE 3.3
Distribution of Students and Average Proficiency in Science Content Areas by Region

	Percent of Students	Life Sciences	Physical Sciences	Earth and Space Sciences	Nature of Science
GRADE 4					
Northeast	22 (0.8)	231 (2.0)	239 (2.5)	237 (1.8)	235 (2.1)
Southeast	24 (0.8)	224 (2.2)	228 (2.5)	226 (2.4)	233 (2.3)
Central	27 (0.8)	232 (2.1)	237 (2.4)	234 (2.4)	232 (2.1)
West	28 (0.8)	229 (2.1)	238 (2.2)	237 (2.1)	234 (2.0)
GRADE 8					
Northeast	21 (1.0)	268 (3.0)	270 (3.3)	270 (3.6)	268 (3.8)
Southeast	24 (0.8)	257 (2.1)	256 (1.7)	257 (2.3)	254 (2.2)
Central	25 (0.7)	265 (1.8)	263 (2.3)	266 (2.1)	263 (2.3)
West	30 (0.9)	264 (3.0)	261 (2.7)	265 (3.1)	258 (2.8)
GRADE 12					
Northeast	24 (1.0)	303 (2.8)	298 (3.8)	298 (3.5)	306 (3.5)
Southeast	21 (0.8)	283 (2.1)	276 (3.6)	272 (2.8)	288 (2.5)
Central	27 (0.5)	298 (2.0)	293 (2.6)	294 (1.8)	298 (2.9)
West	29 (0.9)	298 (2.7)	295 (2.9)	296 (3.5)	301 (3.0)

The standard errors of the estimated percentages and proficiencies appear in parentheses. It can be said with 95 percent certainty that for each population of interest, the value for the whole population is within plus or minus two standard errors of the estimate for the sample.

The 1990 Science Report Card: NAEP's Assessment of Fourth, Eighth, and Twelfth Graders (National Center for Education Statistics, U.S. Department of Education, 1992).

AVERAGE PROFICIENCY IN SCIENCE CONTENT AREAS BY TYPE OF COMMUNITY

TABLE 3.4 presents the average proficiency in the four content areas for students attending schools in advantaged urban, disadvantaged urban, and extreme rural communities as compared to those attending schools in other types of communities. In general, across the four content areas and the three grades assessed, students attending schools in advantaged urban communities tended to have higher average proficiency than students in extreme rural schools or in other types of communities, and the students in these two types of communities tended to perform better than those attending schools in disadvantaged communities.

There were some deviations from this pattern at grade 8 and, particularly, at grade 12. Eighth graders living in disadvantaged urban communities and in extreme rural communities performed similarly in the area of physical sciences. Also, those living in extreme rural communities had lower average proficiency in the area of the nature of science than did those living in communities classified as "other."

At grade 12, students attending schools in disadvantaged urban communities had lower average proficiency than students attending schools in the remaining three types of communities, with two exceptions — in the life sciences and earth and space sciences their performance was not significantly different from that of twelfth graders attending schools in extreme rural communities. Also, even though the pattern of higher performance for advantaged urban students is evident in the results, the differences between their performance and that of students attending schools in extreme rural communities and communities classified as "other" were not statistically significant in any of the four content areas.

TABLE 3.4
Distribution of Students and Average Proficiency in Science Content Areas by Type of Community

	Percent of Students	Life Sciences	Physical Sciences	Earth and Space Sciences	Nature of Science
GRADE 4					
Advantaged Urban	11 (1.7)	245 (2.5)	256 (2.9)	254 (2.5)	251 (2.7)
Disadvantaged Urban	9 (1.1)	205 (2.8)	212 (3.0)	209 (2.7)	211 (2.4)
Extreme Rural	11 (1.8)	233 (2.4)	237 (3.2)	235 (3.1)	235 (2.4)
Other	69 (2.8)	229 (1.1)	235 (1.2)	234 (1.1)	234 (1.2)
GRADE 8					
Advantaged Urban	10 (2.2)!	285 (4.7)!	282 (3.8)!	285 (4.2)!	280 (4.2)!
Disadvantaged Urban	9 (1.7)	243 (3.7)	244 (4.4)	241 (4.8)	237 (4.2)
Extreme Rural	11 (2.1)	257 (3.4)	256 (3.1)	261 (4.1)	252 (3.7)
Other	69 (2.8)	264 (1.3)	263 (1.5)	265 (1.7)	262 (1.6)
GRADE 12					
Advantaged Urban	10 (2.4)!	306 (3.8)!	303 (5.0)!	300 (4.8)!	309 (5.1)!
Disadvantaged Urban	12 (2.5)	278 (4.9)	269 (5.3)	268 (7.1)	278 (4.4)
Extreme Rural	11 (2.7)!	294 (4.1)!	287 (4.0)!	289 (4.0)!	296 (4.4)!
Other	67 (3.5)	298 (1.4)	294 (1.9)	294 (1.7)	301 (1.6)

The standard errors of the estimated percentages and proficiencies appear in parentheses. It can be said with 95 percent certainty that for each population of interest, the value for the whole population is within plus or minus two standard errors of the estimate for the sample.

! Interpret with caution — the nature of the sample does not allow accurate determination of the variability of these estimated statistics.

The 1990 Science Report Card: NAEP's Assessment of Fourth, Eighth, and Twelfth Graders (National Center for Education Statistics, U.S. Department of Education, 1992).

AVERAGE PROFICIENCY IN

SCIENCE CONTENT AREAS

BY TYPE OF SCHOOL   Average proficiency across the content areas for
students attending public, Catholic, and other (non-Catholic) private schools are shown
in TABLE 3.5. At grade 4, students attending private schools — both Catholic and other
private schools — had higher average proficiency than students attending public schools
across all four science content areas. At grade 8, students attending Catholic schools
outperformed public school students across all four science content areas, as did students
attending other private schools in life sciences and earth and space sciences. There were
almost no differences in performance among students attending the different types of
schools at grade 12, although Catholic school students did have higher proficiency than
public school students in the nature of science content area.

TABLE 3.5
Distribution of Students and Average Proficiency in Science Content Areas by Type of School

	Percent of Students	Life Sciences	Physical Sciences	Earth and Space Sciences	Nature of Science
GRADE 4					
Public Schools	89 (1.1)	228 (1.0)	234 (1.2)	232 (1.0)	232 (1.1)
Catholic Schools	7 (0.9)	236 (2.4)	245 (2.3)	243 (2.3)	241 (2.2)
Other Private Schools	5 (0.7)	240 (3.4)	251 (3.5)	248 (3.1)	247 (3.3)
GRADE 8					
Public Schools	89 (1.3)	262 (1.4)	261 (1.3)	263 (1.5)	259 (1.6)
Catholic Schools	7 (1.1)	276 (1.9)	276 (2.2)	276 (2.0)	274 (3.0)
Other Private Schools	4 (0.7)	274 (4.2)	271 (4.0)	277 (3.8)	270 (5.7)
GRADE 12					
Public Schools	90 (1.4)	295 (1.2)	290 (1.7)	290 (1.4)	297 (1.4)
Catholic Schools	5 (1.1)	302 (3.5)	299 (3.8)	298 (3.2)	310 (4.0)
Other Private Schools	4 (1.0)	304 (4.7)	300 (5.8)	299 (4.9)	306 (4.9)

The standard errors of the estimated percentages and proficiencies appear in parentheses. It can be said with 95 percent
certainty that for each population of interest, the value for the whole population is within plus or minus two standard errors of
the estimate for the sample.

The 1990 Science Report Card: NAEP's Assessment of Fourth, Eighth, and Twelfth Graders (National Center for Education Statistics,
U.S. Department of Education, 1992).

AVERAGE PROFICIENCY IN
SCIENCE CONTENT AREAS BY
PARENTS' HIGHEST EDUCATION LEVEL   The relationship
between parents' education level and average science proficiency across the content areas
is presented in TABLE 3.6. The results show a strong, positive relationship between level of
parents' education and average proficiency across all three grades assessed and all four
science content areas. In general, similar to the results presented for overall proficiency in
Chapter One, the more well-educated the parents, the higher the students' average proficiency in each of the four content areas.

At grade 4, students whose parents had post-high school education, including
college degrees, had higher average proficiency in each content area than students whose
parents had not graduated from high school or had graduated from high school, but had
no further schooling. However, it should be noted that approximately one-third of the
students at grade 4 did not know their parents' level of education. At grades 8 and 12,
where nearly all students reported their parents' level of education, the relationship
between parents' education level and average science proficiency in the content areas was
even stronger. For all four content areas, students whose parents had graduated from
college outperformed those students whose parents had some post-high school education,
who, in turn, outperformed students whose parents had no education beyond high school
graduation. Students whose parents had not graduated from high school had the lowest
average proficiency.

OVERALL RELATIONSHIP BETWEEN SCIENCE AND
MATHEMATICS COURSE-TAKING AND
SCIENCE PROFICIENCY, GRADE 12   The first part of this chapter
presented results showing the relationship between performance in the four science
content areas and various background characteristics. The remainder of this chapter will
be devoted to a discussion of the relationship between high school course-taking in the
various content areas and proficiency. However, as an overview, to illustrate the strong
effect that course-taking has on proficiency, TABLE 3.7 shows the direct relationship
between course-taking in science and mathematics, respectively, and overall science
proficiency.

For each successive category of science course-taking, average science proficiency
increased by approximately 20 points. Thus, twelfth graders who had taken eight or more
semesters of science since the ninth grade had higher average proficiency than those who
had taken six to seven semesters. Similarly, those who had taken six to seven semesters of

TABLE 3.6
Distribution of Students and Average Proficiency in Science Content Areas by Parents' Highest Level of Education

	Percent of Students	Life Sciences	Physical Sciences	Earth and Space Sciences	Nature of Science
GRADE 4					
Did Not Finish HS	5 (0.4)	219 (2.7)	223 (3.3)	222 (2.7)	224 (2.3)
Graduated From HS	16 (0.7)	224 (1.7)	227 (1.9)	226 (1.6)	226 (1.6)
Some Education After HS	9 (0.4)	237 (2.2)	247 (2.4)	243 (2.6)	289 (1.8)
Graduated From College	35 (1.1)	238 (1.3)	246 (1.5)	244 (1.3)	243 (1.4)
GRADE 8					
Did Not Finish HS	9 (0.6)	242 (2.8)	239 (2.4)	243 (2.7)	239 (2.4)
Graduated From HS	25 (0.8)	255 (1.6)	254 (1.5)	256 (1.4)	250 (1.7)
Some Education After HS	19 (0.8)	268 (1.5)	268 (1.7)	270 (1.8)	266 (1.5)
Graduated From College	40 (1.6)	277 (2.0)	275 (1.8)	278 (1.7)	275 (1.8)
GRADE 12					
Did Not Finish HS	8 (0.6)	275 (2.8)	265 (3.0)	264 (2.7)	275 (3.0)
Graduated From HS	24 (0.8)	283 (1.4)	274 (1.6)	277 (1.7)	283 (1.9)
Some Education After HS	26 (0.8)	298 (1.4)	291 (1.8)	293 (1.5)	303 (1.7)
Graduated From College	40 (1.3)	309 (1.3)	308 (1.8)	306 (1.8)	312 (1.6)

The standard errors of the estimated percentages and proficiencies appear in parentheses. It can be said with 95 percent certainty that for each population of interest, the value for the whole population is within plus or minus two standard errors of the estimate for the sample. Within each grade, percentages of students do not total 100 percent because some students did not know their parents' highest level of education.

The 1990 Science Report Card: NAEP's Assessment of Fourth, Eighth, and Twelfth Graders (National Center for Education Statistics, U.S. Department of Education, 1992).

TABLE 3.7
Distribution of Students and Average Science Proficiency by Number of Semesters of Science and Mathematics Course-Taking, Grades 9-12

	0-3		4-5		6-7		8 OR MORE	
	Percent of Students	Average Proficiency	Percent of Students	Average Proficiency	Percent of Students	Average Proficiency	Percent of Students	Average Proficiency
Science	28 (1.4)	269 (1.7)	22 (0.8)	290 (1.5)	25 (1.0)	311 (1.7)	25 (1.2)	332 (1.4)
Mathematics	21 (1.1)	265 (2.1)	20 (0.7)	287 (1.6)	23 (0.9)	303 (1.6)	36 (1.1)	324 (1.4)

The standard errors of the estimated percentages and proficiencies appear in parentheses. It can be said with 95 percent certainty that for each population of interest, the value for the whole population is within plus or minus two standard errors of the estimate for the sample.

The 1990 Science Report Card: NAEP's Assessment of Fourth, Eighth, and Twelfth Graders (National Center for Education Statistics, U.S. Department of Education, 1992).

science had higher average proficiency than those who had taken four to five semesters of science and those who had taken zero to three semesters had the lowest average proficiency.

There was a similar relationship between overall science proficiency and the number of semesters of mathematics courses taken since the ninth grade. Those twelfth graders with progressively more mathematics coursework performed much better than those with less coursework.

AVERAGE SCIENCE PROFICIENCY BY SCIENCE COURSE-TAKING   TABLE 3.8 summarizes high school course-taking in biology, chemistry, and physics by race/ethnicity, gender, and for public school and private school students. The comparisons are between those twelfth graders who reported at least one year of study in grades 9 through 12 and those who reported less than one year of study. For biology course-taking, overall average science proficiency is presented as well as average proficiency on the life sciences subscale. For both chemistry and physics, overall average science proficiency is shown as well as average proficiency on the physical sciences subscale.

Several patterns are apparent from Table 3.8. First, almost without exception, across the three types of courses and various subpopulations, the group of high school seniors reporting at least one year of course-taking had higher average science proficiency, both overall and in each particular content area, than did the group reporting less than one year of study.

Second, it can be seen that while most high school seniors had taken at least one year of biology, only about half had taken one year of chemistry and far fewer (29 percent) reported at least one year of physics study. Additionally, there were differences in course-taking, especially in chemistry and physics, by racial/ethnic subgroup, gender, and public/private school status. For example, Asian/Pacific Islander students were more likely to have taken one year or more of both chemistry and physics than were students from other racial/ethnic groups. A greater percentage of private school than public school students reported taking one year or more of both chemistry and physics. Also, higher percentages of males than females had taken physics courses for at least a year.

Finally, in some instances, the differences in proficiency between high- and low-performing groups were larger for students who had taken coursework than for students who had not taken coursework. This was particularly evident in the area of physics course-taking. For example, the gap between White students' average physical science proficiency and that of their Black and Hispanic counterparts was larger for students who had taken physics than for those who had not. These results, and those concerning racial/ethnic and

TABLE 3.8
Average Overall Science Proficiency and Average Content Area Proficiency by Biology, Chemistry, and Physics Course-Taking, Grades 9-12

	ONE YEAR OR MORE			LESS THAN ONE YEAR		
	Percent of Students	Average Proficiency	Average Content Area Proficiency	Percent of Students	Average Proficiency	Average Content Area Proficiency
Biology	91 (1.0)	298 (1.2)	301 (1.1)	9 (1.0)	263 (1.8)	267 (2.1)
White	92 (1.2)	306 (1.2)	308 (1.1)	8 (1.2)	270 (2.6)	274 (3.0)
Black	91 (1.2)	259 (2.6)	265 (2.2)	9 (1.2)	233 (5.4)	240 (5.4)
Hispanic	86 (2.7)	281 (2.8)	283 (2.8)	14 (2.7)	246 (5.5)	247 (6.6)
Asian/Pacific Islander	89 (1.6)	311 (6.0)	312 (6.0)	11 (1.6)	297 (13.8)	298 (14.7)
American Indian	74 (10.0)!	290 (6.5)!	292 (6.9)!	26 (10.0)!	269 (15.2)!	270 (16.7)!
Male	90 (1.2)	305 (1.6)	305 (1.6)	10 (1.2)	268 (3.1)	270 (3.3)
Female	92 (1.0)	292 (1.1)	297 (1.1)	8 (1.0)	257 (2.7)	264 (3.1)
Public Schools	91 (1.1)	298 (1.3)	300 (1.2)	10 (1.1)	262 (2.0)	267 (2.3)
Private Schools	96 (0.7)	303 (3.0)	304 (3.1)	4 (0.7)	275 (5.6)	274 (6.4)
Chemistry	55 (1.3)	314 (1.2)	314 (1.6)	45 (1.3)	273 (1.3)	266 (1.6)
White	56 (1.4)	321 (1.2)	322 (1.6)	44 (1.4)	280 (1.4)	273 (1.8)
Black	49 (3.3)	275 (2.6)	274 (2.9)	51 (3.3)	240 (2.8)	234 (4.1)
Hispanic	48 (3.0)	293 (3.5)	295 (4.5)	52 (3.0)	262 (2.8)	257 (4.1)
Asian/Pacific Islander	80 (7.3)	319 (3.8)	322 (5.1)	20 (7.3)	277 (6.4)	273 (9.4)
American Indian	36 (6.8)!	304 (9.5)!	306 (8.0)!	64 (6.8)!	272 (4.8)!	267 (5.7)!
Male	57 (1.7)	320 (1.8)	324 (2.2)	43 (1.7)	277 (1.6)	272 (2.6)
Female	54 (1.6)	308 (1.2)	306 (1.5)	46 (1.6)	269 (1.7)	261 (1.9)
Public Schools	54 (1.5)	314 (1.4)	315 (1.8)	47 (1.5)	272 (1.3)	265 (1.6)
Private Schools	71 (3.1)	312 (2.9)	312 (3.4)	29 (3.1)	279 (3.1)	271 (3.4)
Physics	29 (1.1)	319 (1.6)	323 (2.1)	71 (1.1)	286 (1.0)	280 (1.2)
White	29 (1.2)	329 (1.6)	334 (2.1)	71 (1.2)	293 (1.0)	287 (1.3)
Black	24 (2.8)	262 (4.5)	262 (5.7)	76 (2.8)	255 (2.6)	251 (3.5)
Hispanic	26 (1.9)	293 (4.1)	294 (4.9)	74 (1.9)	271 (3.4)	268 (4.4)
Asian/Pacific Islander	56 (5.0)	326 (6.2)	333 (7.8)	44 (5.0)	290 (4.2)	285 (5.7)
American Indian	19 (6.0)!	298 (17.8)!	304 (17.2)!	81 (6.0)!	281 (5.2)!	276 (4.6)!
Male	36 (1.3)	324 (2.0)	330 (2.6)	64 (1.3)	289 (1.4)	285 (2.0)
Female	23 (1.2)	312 (2.3)	313 (2.5)	77 (1.2)	283 (1.2)	277 (1.2)
Public Schools	28 (1.1)	319 (1.9)	323 (2.4)	72 (1.1)	285 (1.1)	280 (1.3)
Private Schools	39 (2.9)	318 (4.1)	323 (4.9)	61 (2.9)	291 (3.0)	286 (3.2)

The standard errors of the estimated percentages and proficiencies appear in parentheses. It can be said with 95 percent certainty that for each population of interest, the value for the whole population is within plus or minus two standard errors of the estimate for the sample.

! Interpret with caution — the nature of the sample does not allow accuarte determination of the variability of these estimated statistics.

The 1990 Science Report Card: NAEP's Assessment of Fourth, Eighth, and Twelfth Graders (National Center for Education Statistics, U.S. Department of Education, 1992).

gender differences in course-taking discussed above, tend to confirm a growing body of research indicating that, from kindergarten through high school, many White females and Black and Hispanic males and females have substantially different experiences in science than do White males. For example, they have fewer routine daily experiences with the tools, materials, and equipment of science, they are called on less often in science classes, and schools and society have generally lower expectations regarding their performance.[15]

SUMMARY   The results by science content areas indicated that the differences in performance by racial/ethnic groups apparent in the overall science results presented in Chapter One were also pervasive across the four content areas of life sciences, physical sciences, earth and space sciences, and the nature of science. For each content area, White and Asian/Pacific Islander students had higher average proficiency than did Hispanic and Black students. Also, students attending schools in disadvantaged urban communities had lower average proficiency than their counterparts attending schools in advantaged urban communities across all four content areas. In many cases, disadvantaged urban students had lower average proficiency than students living in any other type of community, including extreme rural areas. Additionally, the strong, positive relationship between level of parents' education and higher average proficiency was evident across all four content areas.

At grade 4, differences in regional performance were less prevalent than they were at grades 8 and 12. At grade 8, students in the Northeast consistently outperformed those in the Southeast. At grade 12, students in the Southeast had lower average proficiency than students in the other three regions of the country in each of the four content areas.

Gender differences in content area proficiency were not as prevalent at grade 4 as at grades 8 and 12. At grade 4, males had higher average proficiency in the area of earth and space sciences, females had higher average proficiency in the area of the nature of science, and there were no gender differences in performance in the other two content areas. At grade 8, however, males also had higher average proficiency than did females in the area of the physical sciences and, at grade 12, they also gained the advantage in the area of the life sciences. It is interesting to note that in contrast to the overall results, females had higher average proficiency than males in the area of the nature of science at all three grade levels.

---

[15] M. C. Linn and J. S. Hyde, Gender, Mathematics and Science, *Educational Researcher* 18 (8):17-27, 1989.

J. B. Kahle and M. K. Lakes, The Myth of Equality in Science Classrooms, *Journal of Research in Science Teaching* 20:131-140, 1983.

Jeannie Oakes, "Opportunities, Achievement, and Choice: Women and Minority Students in Science and Mathematics," in *Review of Research in Education, Volume 16,* ed. C. Cazden (Washington, D.C.: American Educational Research Association, 1990).

At grade 4, students who attended Catholic schools and other private schools had higher proficiency than fourth graders who attended public schools in each of the four content areas. These differences were somewhat less evident at grade 8, and were virtually nonexistent at grade 12.

The NAEP results showed a direct relationship between high school science course-taking and average proficiency. More course work in each content area was related to higher proficiency in that content area and to higher overall science performance. Although most twelfth-grade students reported at least a year of course-taking in biology, only about half reported taking at least a year of chemistry and fewer (29 percent) reported that much physics study. A greater percentage of Asian/Pacific Islander students had taken at least a year of chemistry and physics than their classmates in other racial/ethnic groups as had a greater percentage of private school students, compared to their public school counterparts. More males than females had taken a year or more of physics. Finally, among students who do persevere in school science to the extent of enrolling in physics courses, the data indicate a widening performance gap between White students and their Black and Hispanic counterparts. These results support contentions that educators need to be more aware of the support systems and instructional strategies that lead to more equitable education in science classrooms.

ATTITUDES TOWARD SCIENCE EDUCATION AND STUDENTS' EXPERIENCES IN SCIENCE

*H*ow important is science education to schools and to students? Do students enjoy or dislike science? What experiences do they bring to the formal study of science, and to what extent does school provide relevant experiences? Background questions that were asked of students, their teachers, and the administrators of their schools as part of the 1990 science assessment provide some answers to these questions and insight into the subgroup differences in science proficiency discussed throughout the first three chapters of this report.

Despite the emphasis given to science in many recent national initiatives,[16] science education continues to remain a relatively low priority in our nation's schools. TABLE 4.1 summarizes the percentages of students who attended schools that reported placing a special priority on specific subject areas. Fewer than half of the fourth-grade students attended schools that gave special priority to science, compared to three-fourths or more who attended schools that gave special attention to mathematics, reading, and writing. This relatively lower emphasis on science was also evident at grades 8 and 12. The same low priority surfaced in the most recent Gallup Poll on attitudes toward public schools,[17] which showed that the national education goal emphasizing science and mathematics learning — "By the year 2000, American students will be first in the world in mathematics and science achievement" — received the public's lowest priority ranking among the six national education goals adopted by the President and governors.[18]

TABLE 4.1
Schools' Reports on the Identification of Science as a Priority

PERCENTAGE OF STUDENTS IN SCHOOLS WITH PRIORITIES IN PARTICULAR CURRICULUM AREAS

Has your school identified any of the following subjects as a special priority?	Science	Mathematics	Reading	Writing
Grade 4	45 (2.9)	82 (2.9)	95 (1.7)	78 (2.4)
Grade 8	40 (4.4)	64 (3.6)	76 (3.5)	67 (3.8)
Grade 12	35 (4.1)	57 (4.1)	69 (4.0)	75 (3.0)

The standard errors of the estimated percentages appear in parentheses. It can be said with 95 percent certainty that for each population of interest, the value for the whole population is within plus or minus two standard errors of the estimate for the sample.

The 1990 Science Report Card: NAEP's Assessment of Fourth, Eighth, and Twelfth Graders (National Center for Education Statistics, U.S. Department of Education, 1992).

[16] *Science for all Americans: A Project 2061 Report on Literacy Goals in Science, Mathematics, and Technology* (Washington, D.C.: American Association for the Advancement of Science, 1989).

Educating Scientists and Engineers: Grade School to Grad School (Washington, D.C.: Office of Technology Assessment, 1988).

Fulfilling the Promise: Biology Education in the Nation's Schools (Washington, D.C.: National Research Council, Committee on High-School Biology Education, 1990).

[17] Stanley M. Elam, et al., The 23rd Gallup Poll of the Public's Attitudes Toward the Public Schools, *Phi Delta Kappan* 73(1): 41-56, 1991.

[18] *America 2000: An Education Strategy* (Washington, D.C.: U.S. Department of Education, 1991).

Educating America: State Strategies for Achieving the National Education Goals (Washington, D.C.: National Governors' Association, 1991).

INSTRUCTION AT GRADE 4   That schools do not consider science a

priority is further evidenced by the low frequency of science instruction in elementary

schools. TABLE 4.2 shows fourth-grade students' reports on the frequency of their science

instruction in school. Twenty-eight percent of fourth graders reported having science

instruction about once a week or even less frequently, and only about half reported having

science instruction almost every day.

The importance of frequent science instruction is supported by students' profi-

ciency results. Fourth graders who received science instruction several times a week or

more had higher average proficiency than did students who received science instruction

about once a week, less than once a week, or never. In addition, even those fourth graders

who received only infrequent science instruction — about once a week or less than once a

week — had higher average proficiency than did students who reported never receiving

science instruction.

TABLE 4.2
Fourth-Grade Students' Reports on Frequency of Science Instruction in School

	ALMOST EVERY DAY		SEVERAL TIMES A WEEK		ABOUT ONCE A WEEK		LESS THAN ONCE A WEEK		NEVER	
	% of Students	Avg. Profic.	% of Students	Avg. Profic.	% of Students	Avg. Profic.	% of Students	Avg. Profic.	% of Students	Avg. Profic.
Grade 4	51 (1.9)	235 (1.1)	21 (0.9)	236 (1.5)	14 (1.0)	230 (1.5)	8 (0.7)	227 (2.0)	6 (0.7)	217 (2.8)
Male	51 (1.9)	237 (1.3)	22 (1.1)	237 (2.2)	13 (1.1)	232 (1.9)	8 (0.7)	226 (2.7)	6 (0.8)	218 (3.2)
Female	51 (2.2)	234 (1.3)	20 (1.2)	235 (1.6)	15 (1.3)	228 (2.1)	8 (0.8)	227 (2.6)	5 (0.8)	216 (4.4)
White	54 (2.1)	243 (1.1)	22 (1.1)	246 (1.6)	12 (1.1)	242 (1.7)	8 (0.8)	238 (2.2)	5 (0.8)	230 (3.3)
Black	46 (2.9)	209 (1.8)	20 (1.9)	207 (3.0)	17 (1.7)	203 (1.9)	10 (1.1)	201 (4.0)	7 (1.1)	192 (4.0)
Hispanic	44 (3.4)	216 (2.1)	20 (1.5)	213 (2.2)	18 (1.9)	211 (3.0)	9 (1.0)	205 (2.9)	10 (1.4)	203 (4.0)
Asian/Pacific Islander	39 (5.3)	240 (6.5)	24 (2.6)	230 (4.5)	21 (3.2)	230 (4.1)	8 (2.1)	232 (8.8)	9 (4.1)	223 (10.9)
American Indian	51 (5.0)	228 (3.6)	19 (3.0)	229 (6.8)	13 (3.8)	233 (6.9)	10 (3.2)	216 (8.6)	6 (2.8)	201 (7.6)

The standard errors of the estimated percentages and proficiencies appear in parentheses. It can be said with 95 percent certainty that for each population of interest, the value for the whole population is within plus or minus two standard errors of the estimate for the sample.

The 1990 Science Report Card: NAEP's Assessment of Fourth, Eighth, and Twelfth Graders (National Center for Education Statistics, U.S. Department of Education, 1992).

Each student in the 1990 science assessment was asked to respond to the question "Do you like science?" The results to this inquiry, presented in TABLE 4.3, show that 80 percent of fourth graders reported they liked science and there were no significant differences between the responses of males and females or among students from different racial/ethnic subgroups. Students' affinity for science, however, decreased from elementary school to secondary school. At grade 12, fewer than two-thirds of the students reported liking science, although there continued to be no significant differences in the responses of high school seniors from different racial/ethnic subgroups. In contrast, however, was the difference in the responses of males and females at both grades 8 and 12. At grade 8, 64 percent of females reported liking science, a significantly lower percentage than the 72 percent of males who liked science. At grade 12, only 57 percent of females reported liking science — a substantially lower percentage than the 74 percent of male twelfth graders who reported that they liked science.

As might be expected, at all three grades, the average proficiency of students who reported liking science was higher than the proficiency of students who did not like science. This difference in proficiency between students who did and did not like science also occurred at all three grades for both male and female students and for students in each of the five racial/ethnic subgroups, with the exception of eighth-grade American Indian students, where there was no significant difference in the average proficiency of students who liked science and that of students who did not like science. Interestingly, at grade 8, among students who reported not liking science, females had higher proficiency than males, but among students who reported liking science, males had higher proficiency. Similarly, at grade 12, there was no significant difference in the science proficiency of male and female students who reported not liking science, but among the students who responded that they did like science, males had higher average proficiency than females.

TABLE 4.3
Students' Response to the Question "Do You Like Science?"

	YES		NO	
	Percent of Students	**Average Proficiency**	**Percent of Students**	**Average Proficiency**
GRADE 4	80 (0.8)	237 (1.0)	20 (0.8)	220 (1.4)
Male	81 (1.0)	238 (1.2)	19 (1.0)	218 (2.0)
Female	78 (1.0)	235 (1.2)	22 (1.0)	222 (1.6)
White	81 (0.9)	245 (1.1)	19 (0.9)	231 (1.5)
Black	75 (1.9)	208 (1.7)	25 (1.9)	199 (2.3)
Hispanic	76 (1.4)	217 (1.5)	24 (1.4)	199 (2.5)
Asian/Pacific Islander	78 (5.7)	238 (2.9)	22 (5.7)	217 (4.3)
American Indian	80 (4.1)	230 (3.1)	21 (4.1)	212 (5.1)
GRADE 8	68 (1.0)	269 (1.2)	32 (1.0)	251 (1.4)
Male	72 (1.1)	272 (1.5)	28 (1.1)	248 (2.0)
Female	64 (1.2)	266 (1.5)	36 (1.2)	253 (1.6)
White	67 (1.1)	280 (1.2)	33 (1.1)	258 (1.6)
Black	70 (2.1)	235 (2.3)	30 (2.1)	223 (2.9)
Hispanic	71 (2.1)	245 (2.7)	29 (2.1)	233 (2.9)
Asian/Pacific Islander	70 (4.6)	277 (4.5)	31 (4.6)	256 (5.0)
American Indian	71 (5.9)!	254 (12.5)!	29 (5.9)!	246 (6.8)!
GRADE 12	65 (0.7)	303 (1.3)	35 (0.7)	276 (1.2)
Male	74 (0.9)	307 (1.6)	26 (0.9)	275 (1.9)
Female	57 (1.1)	298 (1.3)	43 (1.1)	277 (1.4)
White	66 (0.9)	312 (1.4)	34 (0.9)	284 (1.3)
Black	60 (1.8)	263 (2.9)	40 (1.8)	247 (3.0)
Hispanic	68 (2.3)	279 (3.0)	32 (2.3)	261 (3.9)
Asian/Pacific Islander	69 (3.5)	320 (7.8)	31 (3.5)	284 (5.0)
American Indian	71 (6.5)!	298 (5.3)!	29 (6.5)!	257 (6.0)!

The standard errors of the estimated percentages and proficiencies appear in parentheses. It can be said with 95 percent certainty that for each population of interest, the value for the whole population is within plus or minus two standard errors of the estimate for the sample.

! Interpret with caution — the nature of the sample does not allow accurate determination of the variability of these estimated statistics.

The 1990 Science Report Card: NAEP's Assessment of Fourth, Eighth, and Twelfth Graders (National Center for Education Statistics, U.S. Department of Education, 1992).

Research evidence shows that meaningful experiences involving science activities and projects facilitate children's learning in science.[19] For this reason, the NAEP student questionnaires probed the extent to which students participated in selected science experiences. Specifically, students were asked whether they had done experiments or projects at home or in school with plants or animals, electricity, chemicals, rocks or minerals, a telescope, and a thermometer or barometer. These results are shown in TABLE 4.4. For each of the six activities, about half of the fourth graders reported that they had conducted the activity either in school or at home, ranging from 58 percent who reported having done projects or experiments with animals or plants to 41 and 42 percent who reported having worked with chemicals and a telescope, respectively. The only notable difference in the responses by gender at the fourth-grade level was in experiences with electricity. Sixty percent of the males, compared to 46 percent of the females, reported having done experiments or projects with electricity. As might be expected, the percentages of students who reported having done each of the six types of experiments or projects increased from grade 4 to grade 8 and from grade 8 to grade 12, reaching approximately 70 to 80 percent for five of the six activities at grade 12. However, the difference between the percentages of males and females in regard to experience with electricity also existed at grades 8 and 12.

Analyses were also conducted in which students were grouped by the number of the six experiments or projects they reported having done (none, 1 or 2, 3 or 4, and 5 or 6). These results, presented in TABLE 4.5, show that only 15 percent of fourth graders, 35 percent of eighth graders, and 55 percent of twelfth graders reported having conducted experiments or projects using at least five of these six very common types of science materials. At grades 4 and 8, similar percentages of males and females reported having used five or six of the listed materials, but at grade 12, a higher percentage of males than females had used five or six of the types of materials.

Some significant differences in the percentages of students who had done five or six of the types of experiments or projects existed across racial/ethnic subgroups at all three grade levels. Perhaps the most striking disparity occurred at grade 8, where 38 percent of White students, compared to 28 percent of Hispanic and 22 percent of Black students, had done experiments using five or six of the materials. Additionally, at grade 12, significant differences existed among students from different types of communities.

[19] Wynne Harlen, *Teaching and Learning Science* (New York: Teachers College Press, 1985).

R. Driver, et al., *Children's Ideas in Science* (Philadelphia, PA: Open University Press, 1985).

TABLE 4.4
Students' Reports on Doing Science Experiments and Projects

AVERAGE PROFICIENCY

Have you ever done experiments or projects at home or in school with . . . ?	Plants or Animals	Electricity	Chemicals	Rocks or Minerals	Telescope	Thermometer or Barometer
GRADE 4	58 (0.8)	53 (1.2)	41 (0.7)	50 (1.2)	42 (0.8)	46 (1.1)
Male	58 (1.0)	60 (1.4)	41 (1.1)	50 (1.2)	43 (1.1)	46 (1.4)
Female	57 (1.3)	46 (1.5)	41 (1.0)	51 (1.7)	41 (1.0)	46 (1.4)
White	58 (1.0)	53 (1.5)	42 (1.0)	51 (1.4)	42 (0.9)	45 (1.3)
Black	53 (1.5)	53 (1.6)	38 (1.8)	47 (1.5)	40 (2.0)	49 (2.0)
Hispanic	57 (1.6)	55 (1.9)	40 (1.5)	47 (1.8)	46 (2.0)	48 (1.8)
Asian/Pacific Islander	64 (3.8)	52 (6.1)	38 (4.7)	48 (5.9)	46 (3.4)	37 (6.0)
American Indian	70 (3.4)	58 (3.6)	39 (4.7)	53 (3.0)	45 (3.9)	57 (3.5)
GRADE 8	72 (1.1)	65 (1.2)	63 (1.4)	58 (1.3)	47 (0.9)	54 (1.2)
Male	71 (1.2)	75 (1.2)	64 (1.5)	57 (1.4)	49 (1.2)	52 (1.3)
Female	73 (1.5)	54 (1.4)	61 (1.6)	59 (1.6)	45 (1.1)	56 (1.6)
White	74 (1.2)	67 (1.4)	65 (1.6)	60 (1.5)	49 (1.1)	56 (1.5)
Black	64 (2.0)	58 (2.5)	57 (2.3)	51 (2.1)	36 (2.3)	47 (2.6)
Hispanic	68 (1.8)	60 (2.3)	55 (1.9)	54 (2.5)	44 (1.7)	49 (2.5)
Asian/Pacific Islander	73 (4.2)	70 (3.0)	64 (3.3)	54 (4.8)	36 (3.3)	46 (5.1)
American Indian	59 (14.4)!	60 (7.8)!	60 (12.5)!	58 (9.2)!	49 (5.0)!	56 (6.4)!
GRADE 12	85 (0.7)	72 (1.0)	81 (0.7)	68 (1.0)	54 (0.8)	69 (1.0)
Male	84 (0.9)	82 (0.9)	83 (0.7)	68 (1.2)	56 (1.1)	70 (1.1)
Female	85 (0.8)	63 (1.4)	80 (1.0)	68 (1.3)	52 (1.1)	69 (1.3)
White	86 (0.7)	74 (1.1)	83 (0.8)	70 (1.0)	55 (1.0)	71 (1.2)
Black	79 (1.8)	65 (2.0)	77 (1.8)	62 (2.3)	51 (2.3)	63 (1.6)
Hispanic	83 (1.9)	64 (2.2)	76 (1.8)	64 (2.5)	53 (2.4)	63 (2.1)
Asian/Pacific Islander	84 (1.9)	74 (2.3)	81 (5.6)	63 (5.2)	49 (3.6)	74 (2.4)
American Indian	78 (7.0)!	72 (9.9)!	74 (7.2)!	61 (5.2)!	42 (8.5)!	62 (6.6)!

The standard errors of the estimated percentages appear in parentheses. It can be said with 95 percent certainty that for each population of interest, the value for the whole population is within plus or minus two standard errors of the estimate for the sample.

! Interpret with caution — the nature of the sample does not allow accurate determination of the variability of these estimated statistics.

The 1990 Science Report Card: NAEP's Assessment of Fourth, Eighth, and Twelfth Graders (National Center for Education Statistics, U.S. Department of Education, 1992).

Sixty-three percent of twelfth graders from advantaged urban communities had used five or six of the materials, while only 47 percent of their counterparts from disadvantaged urban communities had done so.

The number of the six experiments or projects conducted by students was positively related to student proficiency at grades 8 and 12. At both grades, students who had used at least five of the six materials in experiments or projects had higher average profi-

TABLE 4.5
TABLE 4.5
Students' Reports of Number of Types of Science Experiments or Projects

	FIVE OR SIX		THREE OR FOUR		ONE OR TWO		NONE	
	% of Students	Avg. Profic.	% of Students	Avg. Profic.	% of Students	Avg. Profic.	% of Students	Avg. Profic.
GRADE 4	15 (0.6)	239 (1.2)	46 (0.6)	230 (1.2)	32 (0.6)	234 (1.1)	7 (0.5)	235 (1.7)
Male	16 (0.9)	243 (1.7)	47 (1.1)	230 (1.3)	31 (1.1)	235 (1.5)	6 (0.5)	237 (2.9)
Female	13 (0.8)	235 (2.0)	45 (1.1)	230 (1.4)	34 (1.0)	232 (1.3)	8 (0.8)	234 (2.4)
White	16 (0.7)	246 (1.3)	44 (0.8)	240 (1.3)	32 (0.9)	243 (1.2)	8 (0.6)	243 (2.0)
Black	11 (0.9)	212 (3.4)	49 (1.6)	203 (2.0)	33 (1.4)	206 (1.6)	8 (0.9)	213 (3.0)
Hispanic	12 (1.2)	216 (3.2)	51 (1.8)	210 (1.6)	31 (1.3)	215 (1.9)	6 (0.6)	215 (4.2)
Asian/Pacific Islander	15 (5.5)	234 (7.9)	41 (3.4)	231 (4.0)	39 (5.5)	236 (6.1)	4 (1.6)	228 (10.9)
American Indian	17 (2.9)	231 (4.4)	56 (4.2)	225 (3.4)	22 (3.7)	224 (6.0)	5 (1.5)	233 (10.7)
Advantaged Urban	16 (2.0)	257 (3.1)	45 (1.7)	251 (3.1)	33 (2.1)	250 (3.0)	5 (0.9)	250 (6.7)
Disadvantaged Urban	11 (1.3)	212 (4.4)	49 (1.8)	207 (3.2)	32 (1.8)	210 (3.0)	7 (0.9)	214 (5.8)
Extreme Rural	15 (1.9)	238 (3.7)	48 (2.1)	235 (3.0)	29 (1.3)	235 (3.2)	8 (2.1)	231 (7.4)
Other	15 (0.8)	239 (1.6)	45 (0.9)	229 (1.3)	33 (0.9)	234 (1.3)	8 (0.5)	237 (1.7)
GRADE 8	35 (1.3)	277 (1.4)	38 (0.9)	262 (1.3)	22 (0.8)	250 (1.6)	6 (0.4)	238 (2.4)
Male	36 (1.5)	278 (1.6)	38 (0.9)	264 (1.8)	20 (0.9)	252 (1.9)	6 (0.5)	239 (4.0)
Female	33 (1.6)	276 (1.8)	37 (1.2)	261 (1.2)	24 (1.0)	248 (2.1)	6 (0.6)	238 (3.1)
White	38 (1.6)	283 (1.5)	37 (1.0)	272 (1.5)	20 (0.9)	262 (2.1)	5 (0.5)	246 (2.8)
Black	22 (1.9)	246 (3.6)	40 (2.0)	232 (2.4)	32 (1.5)	223 (3.2)	6 (1.1)	216 (6.5)
Hispanic	28 (2.0)	253 (2.8)	40 (1.6)	242 (2.7)	26 (1.7)	234 (2.9)	7 (1.1)	222 (5.0)
Asian/Pacific Islander	29 (3.1)	284 (4.5)	41 (3.2)	270 (4.1)	26 (3.2)	260 (6.1)	5 (1.6)	253 (18.2)
American Indian	34 (10.6)!	266 (5.6)!	35 (6.0)!	251 (10.7)!	20 (9.9)!	245 (6.0)!	11 (3.7)!	223 (9.1)!
Advantaged Urban	44 (5.5)!	293 (4.2)!	36 (4.0)!	281 (3.8)!	16 (1.8)!	267 (2.8)!	4 (0.5)!	264 (7.6)!
Disadvantaged Urban	28 (2.6)	260 (4.6)	39 (1.5)	243 (3.8)	26 (2.2)	227 (4.6)	7 (1.0)	223 (8.1)
Extreme Rural	31 (3.4)	270 (3.5)	34 (2.5)	258 (4.4)	25 (2.6)	248 (5.1)	10 (1.8)	242 (5.8)
Other	34 (1.6)	276 (1.4)	38 (1.0)	263 (1.7)	22 (1.0)	252 (2.2)	5 (0.4)	237 (3.4)

The standard errors of the estimated percentages and proficiencies appear in parentheses. It can be said with 95 percent certainty that for each population of interest, the value for the whole population is within plus or minus two standard errors of the estimate for the sample.

! Interpret with caution — the nature of the sample does not allow accurate determination of the variability of these estimated statistics.

The 1990 Science Report Card: NAEP's Assessment of Fourth, Eighth, and Twelfth Graders (National Center for Education Statistics, U.S. Department of Education, 1992).

TABLE 4.5 (continued)
Students' Reports of Number of
Types of Science Experiments or Projects

	FIVE OR SIX		THREE OR FOUR		ONE OR TWO		NONE	
	% of Students	Avg. Profic.	% of Students	Avg. Profic.	% of Students	Avg. Profic.	% of Students	Avg. Profic.
GRADE 12	55 (1.2)	304 (1.2)	29 (0.8)	288 (1.6)	12 (0.6)	273 (2.2)	4 (0.3)	260 (2.9)
Male	59 (1.3)	308 (1.6)	27 (1.0)	293 (2.1)	10 (0.7)	277 (2.9)	4 (0.4)	266 (4.4)
Female	51 (1.5)	299 (1.3)	31 (1.0)	284 (1.8)	13 (0.9)	270 (2.4)	5 (0.4)	256 (3.8)
White	58 (1.3)	311 (1.1)	28 (0.9)	298 (1.9)	10 (0.6)	282 (2.8)	4 (0.4)	270 (3.6)
Black	46 (2.2)	266 (2.8)	34 (1.7)	253 (3.6)	15 (1.3)	243 (3.9)	6 (0.8)	233 (6.7)
Hispanic	46 (2.1)	283 (2.5)	34 (1.7)	270 (5.2)	16 (1.6)	258 (3.8)	4 (0.9)	238 (9.0)
Asian/Pacific Islander	55 (4.1)	316 (8.6)	27 (2.7)	306 (7.3)	15 (2.1)	289 (7.5)	3 (1.2)	274 (32.2)
American Indian	47 (6.9)!	288 (6.6)!	31 (6.7)!	294 (7.0)!	12 (7.4)!	270 (5.6)!	10 (5.3)!	268 (7.5)!
Advantaged Urban	63 (2.4)!	311 (4.1)!	26 (1.5)!	299 (4.9)!	8 (1.0)!	284 (10.6)!	3 (0.7)!	262 (11.3)!
Disadvantaged Urban	47 (2.9)	286 (4.8)	35 (1.6)	267 (4.7)	13 (1.2)	258 (6.7)	5 (0.7)	238 (10.1)
Extreme Rural	52 (2.6)!	302 (4.1)!	29 (2.4)!	285 (4.9)!	15 (1.2)!	276 (5.6)!	4 (0.6)!	252 (7.5)!
Other	56 (1.5)	305 (1.5)	29 (1.0)	292 (2.1)	11 (0.8)	274 (3.1)	4 (0.4)	266 (3.7)

The standard errors of the estimated percentages and proficiencies appear in parentheses. It can be said with 95 percent certainty that for each population of interest, the value for the whole population is within plus or minus two standard errors of the estimate for the sample.

! Interpret with caution — the nature of the sample does not allow accurate determination of the variability of these estimated statistics.

The 1990 Science Report Card: NAEP's Assessment of Fourth, Eighth, and Twelfth Graders (National Center for Education Statistics, U.S. Department of Education, 1992).

ciency than did students who had used three or four; and these students, in turn, had higher average proficiency than students who had used only one or two of the materials. Students who reported not having conducted any of these experiments had the lowest average science proficiency. This relationship between average student proficiency and the numbers of types of science materials used did not occur at grade 4.

STUDENTS' EXPERIENCES IN SCIENCE CLASSROOMS Eighth and twelfth graders were also asked how frequently they performed several different activities in their science classes and the teachers of the eighth-grade students were asked how frequently their students performed these same activities during science class. Eighth graders' reports and those of their teachers, as well as the results for twelfth-grade students who said they were currently enrolled in a science class, are shown in TABLES 4.6 and 4.7. While most of the activities appear to have occurred at least occasionally for a majority of the students, reading a science textbook was one of the most frequent activities in science classes — 60 percent of eighth-grade students and 46 percent of twelfth-grade students in science classes reported reading their textbooks several times a week or more. Perhaps the most

TABLE 4.6
Students' and Teachers' Reports on Textbooks, Discussions, and Problem Solving in Science Class

When you study science, how often do you. . . ?	PERCENTAGE OF STUDENTS		
	Several Times a Week or More	About Once a Week or Less	Never
Read a Science Textbook			
Grade 8 Students	60 (1.8)	30 (1.2)	10 (1.1)
Grade 12 Science Students	46 (0.9)	29 (0.9)	25 (1.0)
Grade 8 Teachers	54 (3.4)	42 (2.9)	5 (1.6)
Discuss a Science News Event			
Grade 8 Students	34 (1.4)	47 (0.9)	20 (1.2)
Grade 12 Science Students	25 (0.8)	48 (0.9)	27 (1.1)
Grade 8 Teachers	29 (3.3)	71 (3.3)	1 (0.3)
Work on a Science Problem			
Grade 8 Students	41 (1.6)	41 (1.2)	19 (1.2)
Grade 12 Science Students	44 (1.2)	31 (0.9)	25 (1.0)
Grade 8 Teachers	40 (3.5)	57 (3.5)	3 (0.9)

The standard errors of the estimated percentages appear in parentheses. It can be said with 95 percent certainty that for each population of interest, the value for the whole population is within plus or minus two standard errors of the estimate for the sample.

The 1990 Science Report Card: NAEP's Assessment of Fourth, Eighth, and Twelfth Graders (National Center for Education Statistics, U.S. Department of Education, 1992).

disconcerting results occurred at grade 12, where approximately one-fourth of the students reported never discussing a science news event, working on a science problem, or doing a science experiment in their science classes. In addition, about half of the eighth graders and about half of the twelfth graders enrolled in science classes reported never giving an oral or written report in their science classes.

A further examination of eighth-grade students' results by racial/ethnic group revealed that 29 percent of Black students and 26 percent of Hispanic students reported never doing a science experiment, as compared to a significantly lower percentage of White students (19 percent). If, as indicated by the NAEP data, experience with science activities is related to higher achievement, then this result, along with the disparities

TABLE 4.7

Students' and Teachers' Reports on Giving Reports and Doing Experiments in Science Class

When you study science, how often do you. . . ?	PERCENTAGE OF STUDENTS		
	About Once a Week or More	Less Than Once a Week	Never
Give an Oral or Written Science Report			
Grade 8 Students	14 (0.8)	38 (1.7)	49 (1.9)
Grade 12 Science Students	13 (0.7)	34 (1.2)	53 (1.2)
Grade 8 Teachers	15 (2.1)	71 (2.2)	14 (1.8)
Do Science Experiments			
Grade 8 Students	41 (1.8)	38 (1.5)	21 (1.1)
Grade 12 Science Students	51 (1.4)	24 (0.9)	26 (1.1)
Grade 8 Teachers	62 (3.2)	34 (3.0)	4 (1.1)

The standard errors of the estimated percentages appear in parentheses. It can be said with 95 percent certainty that for each population of interest, the value for the whole population is within plus or minus two standard errors of the estimate for the sample.

The 1990 Science Report Card: NAEP's Assessment of Fourth, Eighth, and Twelfth Graders (National Center for Education Statistics, U.S. Department of Education, 1992).

discussed earlier in this chapter regarding the relatively lower percentages of Black and Hispanic students who had done different types of experiments or projects, demonstrates that the very groups of students who should be getting more experiences in science are actually getting less.

The results in TABLES 4.6 and 4.7 also portray large differences between eighth-grade students and their teachers in the perceptions of how frequently different activities are done during science class. For example, 21 percent of the eighth graders reported never doing science experiments. According to their teachers, only 4 percent of these students never did science experiments. Similarly, 49 percent of the eighth-grade students said they never gave oral or written reports, in contrast to their teachers, who indicated that only 14 percent of these students never gave reports in science class.

SUMMARY   Results from student, teacher, and school questionnaires adminis-tered as part of the 1990 science assessment plainly indicate that science is not faring well in our nation's schools. Less than half of the elementary schools and only about one-third of the high schools have identified science education as a special priority despite many national calls for increased emphasis on science in schools. Only half of our nation's fourth graders are receiving science instruction almost every day and more than 25 percent receive science instruction about once a week or less, notwithstanding accumulating evidence, supported by results from this assessment, that shows a positive relationship between frequency of instruction and student science proficiency.

Most students report that they like science, yet the percentage of students who do so decreases from grade 4 to grades 8 and 12. Only slightly more than half of the twelfth-grade students have done experiments or projects using five or six common types of science materials and equipment and the percentages of Black and Hispanic eighth- and twelfth-grade students who have done so are significantly lower than the percentages of their White grade-level counterparts. Reading science textbooks remains a frequent activity in eighth- and twelfth-grade science classes, but about one-fourth of the high-school seniors who were enrolled in a science class reported that they never discussed a science news event, worked on science problems, or did experiments in their science class. More than half reported that they did not give an oral or written report in their science class. These results send a clear message: If students' science achievement is to improve, then school science — particularly meaningful instructional activities in science classes — need to receive additional emphasis.

TOWARD SCIENTIFIC LITERACY FOR ALL: INSTRUCTIONAL GOALS AND PRACTICES

*E*nsuring that all students learn the science they will need to participate fully in our technological society has been accepted as a major goal for science education in the 1990s and beyond.[20] While preparing students for advanced study in science is vitally important, the primary emphasis of several recent science reform initiatives is on developing interest, confidence, and problem-solving abilities on the part of all students.[21] A particularly important correlative goal is to engage more female students and students from underrepresented racial/ethnic groups in science activities and courses that lead to careers in scientific and related technical fields. To what extent are fourth-, eighth-, and twelfth-grade students engaged in various instructional activities in their science classes? What are science teachers' instructional goals? In this

---

[20] *Educating America: State Strategies for Achieving the National Education Goals* (Washington, D.C.: National Governors' Association, 1991).

AMERICA 2000: An Education Strategy (Washington, D.C.: U.S. Departement of Education, 1991).

[21] Bill G. Aldridge, *Essential Changes in Secondary School Science: Scope, Sequence, and Coordination* (Washington, D.C.: National Science Teachers Association, 1989).

Science for All Americans: A Project 2061 Report on Literacy Goals in Science, Mathematics, and Technology (Washington, D.C.: American Association for the Advancement of Science, 1989).

Educating Americans for the 21st Century: A Report to the People and to the National Science Board (Washington, D.C.: National Science Board, 1983).

chapter, these instructional goals and practices in the science classroom are reported, with an emphasis on how current goals and practices relate to the achievement of the goal of scientific literacy for all students.

ABILITY GROUPING IN EIGHTH-GRADE SCIENCE CLASSES   Traditionally, students have often been grouped for instruction by their level of ability. This practice is based on the assumption that students learn best when grouped homogeneously by ability because the teacher can better align instruction to the level of the group. Alternatively, some research evidence has demonstrated both the ineffectiveness of ability grouping and the feasibility of heterogeneous grouping as an alternative.[22] For example, because economically disadvantaged students may start school at an educational disadvantage, they are often perceived as lacking in academic ability and are likely to be placed in low-level classes where instruction is conceptually simplified, proceeds at a slower pace, and exposes them to less content.[23]

TABLE 5.1
Eighth-Grade Science Teachers' Reports on Ability Grouping

REPORTS ON THE PREVALENCE OF ABILITY GROUPING IN SCIENCE CLASSES:

YES, STUDENTS GROUPED BY ABILITY		NO, STUDENTS NOT GROUPED BY ABILITY	
Percent of Students	Average Proficiency	Percent of Students	Average Proficiency
25 (3.0)	269 (3.0)	75 (3.0)	266 (1.7)

REPORTS ON ABILITY LEVELS OF SCIENCE CLASSES:

PRIMARILY HIGH ABILITY		PRIMARILY AVERAGE ABILITY		PRIMARILY LOW ABILITY		ABILITY MIXED WIDELY	
Percent of Students	Average Proficiency	Percent of Students	Average Proficiency	Percent of Students	Average Proficiency	Percent of Students	Average Proficiency
16 (1.4)	290 (1.9)	36 (2.2)	267 (1.4)	11 (1.7)	244 (3.7)	37 (3.0)	263 (2.8)

The standard errors of the estimated percentages and proficiencies appear in parentheses. It can be said with 95 percent certainty that for each population of interest, the value for the whole population is within plus or minus two standard errors of the estimate for the sample.

The 1990 Science Report Card: NAEP's Assessment of Fourth, Eighth, and Twelfth Graders (National Center for Education Statistics, U.S. Department of Education, 1992).

[22] A. Gamoran and M. Berends, The Effects of Stratification in Secondary Schools: Synthesis of Survey and Ethnographic Research, *Review of Education Research* 57: 415-435, 1987.

[23] Curtis C. McKnight, et al., *The Underachieving Curriculum: Assessing U.S. School Mathematics from an International Perspective* (Champaign, IL: Stipes Publishing Co., 1987).

As part of the 1990 science assessment, science teachers of eighth-grade students were asked whether students were assigned to their science classes by ability. These results are presented in TABLE 5.1. According to their teachers, only about one-fourth of the eighth graders were assigned to science classes based on ability level. Nevertheless, also according to teachers, most students were in homogeneously grouped science classes. As shown in TABLE 5.1, 36 percent of the students were in classes comprised of primarily average-ability students, 16 percent were in primarily high-ability classes, and 11 percent were in primarily low-ability science classes, as compared to 37 percent in science classes that included students of widely mixed ability levels.

SCIENCE CONTENT EMPHASIS IN EIGHTH-GRADE SCIENCE CLASSES

As part of the focus on scientific literacy for all students, several major projects are attempting to define what students should know and be able to do in science by the time they complete high school. Project 2061, a major undertaking of the American Association for the Advancement of Science, is based on the premise that, rather than trying to teach more and more content, science instruction should focus on building interconnections between key scientific concepts generally taught within separate courses.[24] The Scope, Sequence, and Coordination project of the National Science Teachers Association aims to replace the traditional curriculum, in which life, physical, and earth sciences are taught as distinct courses, with a curriculum in which each of these major disciplines of science is studied every year from grades 7 through 12.[25] In this curriculum, science content would be sequenced in a developmentally appropriate way, proceeding from the concrete to the abstract. A science curriculum proposed by the National Center for Improving Science Education in its report, The High Stakes of High School Science, recommends that all students take a core science curriculum through grade 10. This approach would embody a fundamental, integrated understanding of the traditional scientific disciplines, followed by two years in which students could choose either an academic or a technology-oriented course of science study.[26]

As shown in TABLE 5.2, the curricula proposed in these reforms have not yet been incorporated into schools' science programs. Eighty-three percent of all eighth-grade students were enrolled in discipline-specific science classes, with 51 percent enrolled in

[24] *Science for All Americans: A Project 2061 Report on Literacy Goals in Science, Mathematics, and Technology* (Washington, D.C.: American Association for the Advancement of Science, 1989).

[25] Bill G. Aldridge, *Essential Changes in Secondary School Science: Scope, Sequence, and Coordination* (Washington, D.C.: National Science Teachers Association, 1989).

[26] *The High Stakes of High School Science* (Washington, D.C.: National Center for Improving Science Education, 1991).

TABLE 5.2
Eighth-Grade Science Teachers' Reports on the Content Emphasis of Their Science Courses

PERCENTAGE OF STUDENTS					
What best describes the content of this course?	General Science	Life Science	Physical Science	Earth Science	Integrated Science
GRADE 8	11 (2.6)	7 (2.0)	25 (3.6)	51 (4.8)	6 (1.7)
Advantaged Urban	9 (5.6)	16 (9.4)	29 (9.6)	43 (6.8)	3 (3.0)
Disadvantaged Urban	5 (3.1)	2 (1.3)	30 (8.7)	56 (10.4)	7 (1.7)
Extreme Rural	4 (3.0)!	12 (11.4)!	30 (15.7)!	50 (16.8)!	6 (5.5)!
Other	13 (3.5)	6 (1.6)	23 (3.9)	52 (6.0)	7 (2.1)

The standard errors of the estimated percentages and proficiencies appear in parentheses. It can be said with 95 percent certainty that for each population of interest, the value for the whole population is within plus or minus two standard errors of the estimate for the sample.

! Interpret with caution — the nature of the sample does not allow accurate determination of the variability of these estimated statistics.

The 1990 Science Report Card: NAEP's Assessment of Fourth, Eighth, and Twelfth Graders (National Center for Education Statistics, U.S. Department of Education, 1992).

classes that emphasized earth science and 25 percent in classes that emphasized physical science. Seventeen percent of the students were enrolled in science courses described as general or integrated. This same emphasis on earth science or physical science content occurred regardless of whether students attended schools in advantaged urban, disadvantaged urban, extreme rural, or other types of communities.

TEACHERS' INSTRUCTIONAL GOALS IN EIGHTH-GRADE SCIENCE CLASSES   While there is not yet agreement in the science education community about the specific science content that should be taught at each grade, consensus is emerging on some major points, including support for the contention that "less is more," i.e., that the emphasis in science classes should be on students' in-depth understanding of a smaller number of important concepts rather than on the more superficial knowledge of a myriad of facts and definitions.[27] Similarly, there is consensus about the importance of students' abilities to apply science content to situations they know and care about, including applications in daily life, in technology, and to issues of societal concern. Over the next two years, standards for science curricula are to be developed under the aegis of the National Academy of Sciences.

[27] *Science Framework for the 1994 National Assessment of Educational Progress* (Washington, D.C.: National Assessment Governing Board, U.S. Department of Education, 1992).

1990 Science Framework for California Public Schools: Kindergarten Through Grade Twelve (Sacramento, CA: California Department of Education, 1990).

While these standards are being developed, what are teachers attempting to achieve with their science instruction? As part of NAEP's 1990 science questionnaires, science teachers of eighth graders were asked to indicate the degree of emphasis that they gave to each of a number of instructional objectives for their science classes. TABLE 5.3 shows the percentages of eighth-grade students whose teachers reported placing heavy, moderate, little, or no emphasis on each of a number of instructional objectives. These responses indicate that teachers apply some but not all of the tenets of the science curricular reforms.

TABLE 5.3
Eighth-Grade Science Teachers' Reports of Emphasis on Various Instructional Objectives in Science Class

Instructional Objective	PERCENTAGE OF STUDENTS			
	Heavy Emphasis	Moderate Emphasis	Little Emphasis	No Emphasis
Understanding key science concepts	86 (1.9)	14 (1.9)	0 (0.1)	0 (0.0)
Developing interest in science	61 (2.7)	37 (2.7)	2 (0.6)	0 (0.0)
Developing confidence in ability to understand science and apply that understanding	58 (3.0)	38 (2.9)	5 (1.2)	0 (0.0)
Developing problem-solving skills	54 (3.0)	41 (3.1)	6 (1.8)	0 (0.0)
Knowing science facts and terminology	46 (2.7)	51 (2.5)	3 (1.1)	0 (0.0)
Understanding the application of science in industry and everyday life	45 (3.1)	45 (3.4)	10 (1.8)	0 (0.2)
Learning about the relevance of science to society	45 (3.1)	44 (3.4)	11 (1.9)	0 (0.1)
Preparing for further study in science	43 (2.4)	48 (2.7)	9 (1.8)	0 (0.2)
Knowing how to communicate ideas in science effectively	38 (2.1)	44 (2.6)	17 (2.3)	1 (0.4)
Developing skills in laboratory techniques	38 (2.7)	39 (2.3)	21 (2.1)	3 (0.9)
Understanding the nature of science as a discipline	21 (2.3)	50 (2.9)	27 (2.7)	2 (0.7)

The standard errors of the estimated percentages appear in parentheses. It can be said with 95 percent certainty that for each population of interest, the value for the whole population is within plus or minus two standard errors of the estimate for the sample.

The 1990 Science Report Card: NAEP's Assessment of Fourth, Eighth, and Twelfth Graders (National Center for Education Statistics, U.S. Department of Education, 1992).

Eighth-grade science teachers concurred with reformers that conceptual knowledge is important — virtually all eighth graders had teachers who placed heavy or moderate emphasis on developing an understanding of important science concepts. Also, 90 percent of the students had teachers who placed heavy or moderate emphasis on the applications of science in industry and everyday life. However, 97 percent of eighth-grade students attended science classes where teachers continued to place heavy or moderate emphasis on knowing science facts and terminology. In addition, about one-fourth of the students attended classes that placed little or no emphasis on developing skills in laboratory techniques or on the understanding of the nature of science as a discipline.

TEACHERS' INSTRUCTIONAL PRACTICES IN SCIENCE CLASSROOMS

While curricula and instructional emphasis may be mandated to some extent by state and district curriculum guidelines, responses collected from teachers as part of the 1990 assessment indicate that what teachers choose to emphasize cannot be attributed primarily to those influences. As shown in TABLE 5.4, a large majority of eighth graders are taught science by teachers who reported that they had a great deal of freedom in making decisions about the way they taught their science classes, and 60 percent had science teachers who reported having a great deal of freedom in making decisions about curriculum. Yet nearly half of the eighth graders had science teachers who chose to rely on textbooks to determine what they teach. This may not be surprising in view of the fact that nearly 40 percent of the students had teachers who indicated that their facilities for teaching laboratory science were inadequate. Additionally, 35 percent of the students had teachers who reported that they were poorly supplied with materials and resources.

TABLE 5.4

Eighth-Grade Science Teachers' Reports on Curriculum Decisions and Instructional Resources

	STRONGLY AGREE/ AGREE		NO OPINION		DISAGREE/ STRONGLY DISAGREE	
	Percent of Students	Average Proficiency	Percent of Students	Average Proficiency	Percent of Students	Average Proficiency
I have a great deal of freedom in making decisions about the way I teach my science classes.	91 (1.9)	265 (1.4)	2 (0.6)	257 (8.1)	7 (1.4)	266 (3.2)
My facilities for teaching laboratory science are adequate.	56 (3.0)	267 (2.0)	6 (1.5)	267 (4.3)	39 (2.8)	263 (1.8)
I am well supplied with instructional materials and resources.	56 (3.1)	269 (1.6)	9 (1.8)	261 (5.0)	35 (3.0)	261 (2.0)
I have a great deal of freedom in making decisions about curriculum.	59 (3.3)	266 (1.7)	12 (1.9)	264 (3.2)	29 (2.7)	264 (2.1)
I rely primarily on textbooks to determine what I teach.	48 (3.0)	262 (1.9)	7 (1.3)	269 (3.1)	46 (3.0)	268 (2.1)

The standard errors of the estimated percentages and proficiencies appear in parentheses. It can be said with 95 percent certainty that for each population of interest, the value for the whole population is within plus or minus two standard errors of the estimate for the sample.

The 1990 Science Report Card: NAEP's Assessment of Fourth, Eighth, and Twelfth Graders (National Center for Education Statistics, U.S. Department of Education, 1992).

Teachers were also provided with list of possible science class activities and asked to indicate those that took place during their most recent lesson in their eighth-grade science classes. The results are summarized in FIGURE 5.1.

As was the case with middle/junior high school science classes in both 1977 and 1985-86,[28] most eighth graders' science classes in 1990 included lecture (84 percent) and discussion (91 percent). Other activities, including teacher demonstrations, reading about science, small group work, and work with hands-on materials were somewhat less common. Very few students did field work or used computers during their most recent science class.

[28] Iris R. Weiss, *Science and Mathematics Education Briefing Book* (Chapel Hill, NC: Horizon Research, Inc., 1989).

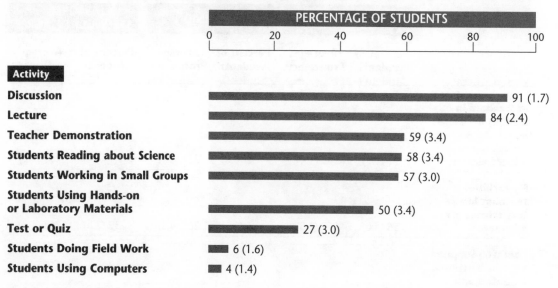

FIGURE 5.1
Eighth-Grade Science Teachers' Reports of Activities Used in Their Most Recent Science Class

PERCENTAGE OF STUDENTS

0   20   40   60   80   100

Activity

Activity	Value
Discussion	91 (1.7)
Lecture	84 (2.4)
Teacher Demonstration	59 (3.4)
Students Reading about Science	58 (3.4)
Students Working in Small Groups	57 (3.0)
Students Using Hands-on or Laboratory Materials	50 (3.4)
Test or Quiz	27 (3.0)
Students Doing Field Work	6 (1.6)
Students Using Computers	4 (1.4)

The standard errors of the estimated percentages appear in parentheses. It can be said with 95 percent certainty that for each population of interest, the value for the whole population is within plus or minus two standard errors of the estimate for the sample.

The 1990 Science Report Card: NAEP's Assessment of Fourth, Eighth, and Twelfth Graders (National Center for Education Statistics, U.S. Department of Education, 1992).

Eighth-grade students and those twelfth-grade students who were enrolled in a science course were asked how frequently their teachers used several different instructional approaches in their science class. The science teachers of the eighth graders were also asked how frequently they used some of these approaches. The responses, which are summarized in TABLE 5.5, reveal that a majority of students at both grades 8 and 12 reported that their teachers lectured in science class several times a week or more. About 40 percent of eighth graders and 50 percent of twelfth graders reported that their teachers demonstrated scientific principles or asked about reasons for experimental results several times a week or more, as compared to the approximately 30 percent of the students at both grade levels who stated that their teachers asked for an opinion on a science issue that frequently. Nearly half of the eighth graders and one-third of the twelfth graders reported that their teachers never asked them to write up an experiment, and 79 percent of eighth graders and 68 percent of twelfth graders reported that they never used computers in science class.

TABLE 5.5
Students' and Teachers' Reports on Teachers' Instructional Approaches in Science Class

In science class, how often does your teacher. . . ?	SEVERAL TIMES A WEEK OR MORE		ABOUT ONCE A WEEK OR LESS		NEVER	
	Percent of Students	Average Proficiency	Percent of Students	Average Proficiency	Percent of Students	Average Proficiency
Lecture						
Grade 8 Students	61 (1.0)	270 (1.2)	27 (0.9)	263 (1.6)	13 (0.6)	238 (2.1)
Grade 12 Science Students	76 (0.8)	307 (1.4)	13 (0.7)	286 (2.2)	11 (0.6)	259 (2.2)
Grade 8 Teachers	59 (3.2)	265 (1.5)	41 (3.2)	267 (2.0)	1 (0.3)	257 (4.6)
Demonstrate a scientific principle						
Grade 8 Students	42 (1.1)	266 (1.4)	41 (1.0)	272 (1.3)	17 (0.8)	239 (1.8)
Grade 12 Science Students	56 (1.0)	305 (1.3)	32 (0.8)	301 (2.0)	12 (0.6)	261 (2.2)
Grade 8 Teachers	30 (3.0)	268 (3.1)	69 (3.0)	265 (1.5)	1 (0.4)	275 (4.6)
Ask about reasons for experimental results						
Grade 8 Students	40 (1.3)	266 (1.6)	44 (1.0)	269 (1.3)	17 (1.0)	246 (2.3)
Grade 12 Science Students	48 (1.0)	303 (1.6)	39 (0.8)	304 (1.9)	13 (0.6)	266 (2.0)
Ask you to write up an experiment						
Grade 8 Students	13 (0.7)	249 (2.9)	39 (1.2)	270 (1.5)	48 (1.4)	263 (1.4)
Grade 12 Science Students	18 (0.8)	295 (2.5)	51 (1.1)	309 (1.5)	32 (1.4)	284 (2.0)
Grade 8 Teachers	16 (2.5)	270 (4.2)	77 (2.9)	266 (1.2)	7 (1.5)	258 (4.8)
Ask for an opinion on a science issue						
Grade 8 Students	32 (1.0)	263 (1.6)	42 (0.7)	269 (1.2)	26 (1.1)	258 (1.9)
Grade 12 Science Students	30 (1.0)	295 (1.7)	43 (0.9)	306 (1.6)	27 (1.1)	291 (2.0)
Ask you to use computers						
Grade 8 Students	6 (0.5)	226 (3.3)	15 (1.0)	264 (3.1)	79 (1.2)	267 (1.2)
Grade 12 Science Students	7 (0.5)	278 (3.1)	25 (1.1)	305 (2.3)	68 (1.2)	298 (1.3)

The standard errors of the estimated percentages and proficiencies appear in parentheses. It can be said with 95 percent certainty that for each population of interest, the value for the whole population is within plus or minus two standard errors of the estimate for the sample.

The 1990 Science Report Card: NAEP's Assessment of Fourth, Eighth, and Twelfth Graders (National Center for Education Statistics, U.S. Department of Education, 1992).

Eighth-grade students' responses regarding their teachers' instructional approaches differed significantly from their teachers' responses in several instances. For example, according to the teachers, only 7 percent of the eighth graders were never asked to write up an experiment, while 48 percent of the students reported never doing this activity.

Eighth and twelfth graders' average proficiency in relation to their participation in the various science class activities is not clear cut. However, those who reported never listening to lectures, watching their teachers perform demonstrations, or being asked to explain reasons for experimental results did have lower average proficiency than their classmates who reported at least some participation in these activities.

Working on science projects over an extended period of time can provide students

TABLE 5.6
Students' and Teachers' Reports on Science Projects that Take a Week or More

	YES		NO	
	Percent of Students	**Average Proficiency**	**Percent of Students**	**Average Proficiency**
Do you ever do science projects in school that take a week or more?				
Grade 4 Students	54 (1.2)	235 (1.1)	46 (1.2)	232 (1.1)
Grade 8 Students	59 (1.5)	268 (1.3)	41 (1.5)	257 (1.6)
Grade 12 Science Students	44 (1.4)	308 (1.6)	57 (1.4)	291 (1.5)
Do you ever assign science projects that take a week or more?				
Grade 8 Teachers	72 (3.1)	266 (1.7)	28 (3.1)	266 (2.6)

The standard errors of the estimated percentages appear in parentheses. It can be said with 95 percent certainty that for each population of interest, the value for the whole population is within plus or minus two standard errors of the estimate for the sample.

The 1990 Science Report Card: NAEP's Assessment of Fourth, Eighth, and Twelfth Graders (National Center for Education Statistics, U.S. Department of Education, 1992).

with an opportunity to apply their knowledge of science to the solution of a practical problem in a way that more closely approximates the way that scientists work than does a single classroom laboratory session. As can be seen in the results presented in TABLE 5.6, more than half of the students at grades 4 and 8 reported that they worked on science projects in school that took a week or more, and fewer than half of the twelfth graders in science classes reported doing such projects. At each of the three grades, students who reported having completed longer science projects performed better than those who had not done so.

HOW MUCH SCIENCE HOMEWORK

DO STUDENTS DO?
One way to extend the instruction that takes place in school is through homework. Students' and eighth-grade teachers' reports of the amount of time spent doing science homework each week are presented in TABLE 5.7. The results indicate that relatively few students at any of the three grades spend a substantial amount of time on science homework. At grade 4, about one-third of the students reported spending no time on science homework each week and only one-fifth reported spending one hour or more, as compared to the 36 percent of eighth graders who spent one or more hours on homework.

TABLE 5.7
Students' and Teachers' Reports on Weekly Time Spent on Science Homework

	NONE		ONE-HALF HOUR		ONE HOUR	
	Percent of Students	Average Proficiency	Percent of Students	Average Proficiency	Percent of Students	Average Proficiency
Grade 4 Students	32 (1.0)	236 (1.1)	42 (1.2)	237 (1.1)	14 (0.6)	229 (1.5)
Grade 8 Students	20 (1.2)	251 (1.8)	41 (0.7)	264 (1.2)	20 (0.7)	267 (1.6)
Grade 12 Science Students	41 (1.3)	281 (1.5)	19 (0.8)	297 (1.9)	16 (0.7)	305 (2.2)
Grade 8 Teachers	1 (0.2)	245 (9.7)	10 (2.1)	259 (5.3)	33 (2.9)	266 (2.3)

	TWO HOURS		MORE THAN TWO HOURS	
	Percent of Students	Average Proficiency	Percent of Students	Average Proficiency
Grade 4 Students	3 (0.2)	220 (2.6)	3 (0.2)	213 (2.7)
Grade 8 Students	9 (0.5)	277 (1.9)	7 (0.5)	272 (2.6)
Grade 12 Science Students	11 (0.6)	318 (2.4)	14 (0.9)	326 (2.1)
Grade 8 Teachers	39 (3.6)	267 (1.9)	18 (2.4)	270 (3.6)

The standard errors of the estimated percentages and proficiencies appear in parentheses. It can be said with 95 percent certainty that for each population of interest, the value for the whole population is within plus or minus two standard errors of the estimate for the sample. Percentages of Grade 4 students and Grade 8 students do not total 100 percent because small percentages of students at both grades reported that they did not have a science class.

The 1990 Science Report Card: NAEP's Assessment of Fourth, Eighth, and Twelfth Graders (National Center for Education Statistics, U.S. Department of Education, 1992).

At grade 8, students who spent at least one-half hour on science homework per week had higher average proficiency levels than those who spent no time on science homework. However, eighth graders did not report doing nearly the amount of science homework per week that their teachers said they did. For example, 61 percent of the eighth graders reported spending only one-half hour or less on science homework per week and only 16 percent reported doing science homework for two hours or more. In contrast, their teachers reported that only 11 percent of the students spent one-half hour or less per week on science homework and that the majority (57 percent) were spending at least two hours, if not more time, on science homework.

At grade 12, there was a direct positive relationship between average science proficiency and time spent on homework, according to students' own reports. However, a surprisingly high percentage of twelfth-grade students taking science courses — 41 percent — reported spending no time on science homework. Only one-fourth of these high school seniors reported spending at least two hours per week — roughly less than one-half hour per day — on their science homework.

SUMMARY   If traditional science educational practices must be changed in order to ensure that all students achieve scientific literacy by the time they leave high school, as the national reform efforts discussed in this chapter contend, then results from the 1990 NAEP science assessment indicate that change in ongoing instructional practices should occur. According to teachers, eighth-grade science classrooms tended to maintain the traditional grouping of students by ability — 63 percent of eighth graders were grouped for instruction by ability. Most eighth-grade science classes also appeared to maintain a subject-specific content base, with more than three-fourths of the students taking classes that emphasized either earth science or physical science and 17 percent taking classes described as general or integrative.

Most eighth-grade science students were taught by teachers who placed heavy or moderate emphasis on understanding key concepts and the practical applications of science. However, 97 percent of eighth graders were taught by teachers who placed heavy or moderate emphasis on knowing scientific facts and terminology and about one-fourth were taught by teachers who put little or no emphasis on developing skills in laboratory techniques or on fostering an understanding of the nature of science. A large majority of eighth graders were taught by teachers who felt that they had a great deal of freedom to make decisions about how they teach science, suggesting that some reforms could take hold at the level of the individual classroom. However, nearly half of the eighth-grade students had teachers who reported relying primarily on textbooks to determine what they taught. Also, more than one-third of the eighth-graders were taught by teachers who felt that their science laboratory facilities and instructional materials were inadequate.

Teachers' instructional approaches in science classrooms often focused on some traditional practices. A large majority of eighth-grade students — 84 percent — were taught by teachers who lectured in their most recent science class, compared to the 57 percent and 50 percent whose most recent science class involved work in small groups or the use of hands-on laboratory materials, respectively. Nearly half of the eighth graders and about one-third of the twelfth graders in science classes reported that their teachers never asked them to write up an experiment. Slightly more than half of the fourth-grade and eighth-grade students reported that they had done science projects that took a week or more, although fewer than half of the high school seniors taking science had done such projects. At all three grades, students who had worked on an extended science project had higher average proficiency than students who had not done so.

At grade 12, increases in amounts of time spent on science homework were related to progressively higher average science proficiency, and at grade 8, students who spent at least some time on science homework had higher proficiency than those who spent no time on science homework. However, effort spent on homework at any of the three grades was not substantial. Only 20 percent of fourth graders and 36 percent of eighth graders reported spending one hour or more on science homework each week. Also, eighth graders reported spending far less time on their science homework than their teachers seemed to think they did. Furthermore, 41 percent of twelfth graders currently taking science reported spending no time on science homework each week.

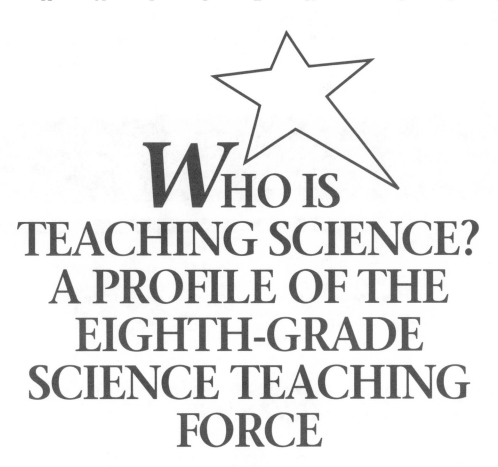

WHO IS TEACHING SCIENCE? A PROFILE OF THE EIGHTH-GRADE SCIENCE TEACHING FORCE

*T*he quality of science education depends to a large extent on the capabilities of the teachers assigned to teach science. This chapter describes the eighth-grade science teaching force, including information about teacher preparation for teaching science and demographic information, such as gender and race/ethnicity. This information was collected by means of a teacher questionnaire administered to the science teachers of the eighth graders included in the NAEP sample. Results are presented showing the percentages of students taught by teachers with particular characteristics.

GENDER AND RACE/ETHNICITY   TABLE 6.1 summarizes the percentages of eighth-grade students taught by male, female, White, Black, Hispanic, and Asian/Pacific Islander science teachers. In general, these data and data presented later in this chapter regarding teachers' years of experience and undergraduate degrees parallel results from the 1987-88 Schools and Staffing Survey (SASS) conducted by the U.S. Department of Education's National Center for Education Statistics.[29] The data show that 55

103

[29] *Selected Characteristics of Public and Private School Teachers: 1987-88*, National Center for Education Statistics, E.D. Tabs (Washington, D.C.: U.S. Department of Education, July 1990).

percent of the eighth graders were taught science by males and 45 percent by females. Ninety percent of all eighth graders were taught by White science teachers and 95 percent of the nation's White eighth graders were taught science by White teachers. In contrast, 28 percent of Black eighth graders had Black science teachers, 6 percent of Hispanic eighth

TABLE 6.1
Eighth-Grade Science Teachers' Reports on Their Gender and Race/Ethnicity

| | TEACHERS' GENDER | | TEACHERS' RACE/ETHNICITY | | | |
| | MALE | FEMALE | WHITE | BLACK | HISPANIC | ASIAN/ PACIFIC ISLANDER |
	Percent of Students	Percent of Students	Percent of Students	Percent of Students	Percent of Students	Percent of Students
Grade 8 Students	55 (3.0)	45 (3.0)	90 (1.5)	8 (1.2)	2 (0.8)	1 (0.4)
Male	55 (3.4)	45 (3.4)	89 (1.7)	8 (1.4)	2 (0.9)	1 (0.4)
Female	54 (3.1)	46 (3.1)	90 (1.5)	8 (1.1)	2 (0.8)	1 (0.4)
White	58 (3.3)	43 (3.3)	95 (1.2)	4 (0.8)	1 (0.7)	0 (0.1)
Black	41 (5.7)	59 (5.7)	70 (4.8)	28 (4.7)	1 (0.4)	2 (1.1)
Hispanic	51 (3.1)	49 (3.1)	82 (3.9)	9 (2.1)	6 (3.3)	2 (1.2)
Asian/Pacific Islander	56 (8.9)	45 (8.9)	86 (5.0)	7 (3.5)	1 (1.1)	6 (3.6)

The standard errors of the estimated percentages appear in parentheses. It can be said with 95 percent certainty that for each population of interest, the value for the whole population is within plus or minus two standard errors on the estimate for the sample. When the percentage of students is either 0 or 100, the standard error is inestimable. However, percentages 99.5 percent and greater were rounded to 100 percent, and percentages less than 0.5 percent were rounded to 0 percent. Data are not presented for American Indian students because breakdown by teachers' race/ethnicity resulted in too few students in each category.

graders had Hispanic science teachers, and 6 percent of Asian/Pacific Islander students had Asian/Pacific Islander science teachers. Although some research evidence has indicated that minority students may benefit from having teachers who serve as positive minority role models, these results show that there are relatively few Black, Hispanic, or Asian/Pacific Islander eighth-grade science teachers.[30]

YEARS OF TEACHING EXPERIENCE   The eighth-grade science teaching force is an experienced one, as shown by the data presented in TABLE 6.2. Eighth-grade science teachers reported an average of 14 years of elementary or secondary teaching experience and an average of 12 years of experience teaching science. This level of experience is comparable to the number of years of experience reported by eighth-grade mathematics teachers in 1990, who reported an average of 16 years overall teaching experience and 14 years of experience teaching mathematics.[31] However, while more than one-third

[30] Shirley McBay, *Increasing the Number and Quality of Minority Science and Mathematics Teachers* (New York: Carnegie Forum on Education and the Economy, 1986).

[31] Ina V.S. Mullis, et al., *The State of Mathematics Achievement: NAEP's 1990 Assessment of the Nation and the Trial Assessment of the States* (Washington, D.C.: U.S. Department of Education, 1991).

		ELEMENTARY/SECONDARY TEACHING EXPERIENCE					
		5 YEARS OR LESS EXPERIENCE		**MORE THAN 5 YEARS, LESS THAN 15 YEARS EXPERIENCE**		**15 YEARS OR MORE EXPERIENCE**	
	Avg. Yrs. Teaching	**Percent of Students**	**Average Proficiency**	**Percent of Students**	**Average Proficiency**	**Percent of Students**	**Average Proficiency**
Total	14 (0.6)	24 (2.6)	264 (2.8)	30 (3.2)	263 (1.9)	46 (2.9)	267 (1.6)
Male		23 (2.6)	265 (2.9)	31 (3.6)	264 (2.4)	46 (3.3)	271 (2.0)
Female		25 (2.8)	263 (3.5)	29 (3.0)	263 (2.1)	45 (2.8)	264 (1.7)
White		24 (2.9)	274 (2.5)	30 (3.8)	271 (2.7)	47 (3.3)	276 (1.5)
Black		28 (5.0)	233 (5.6)	30 (3.3)	235 (3.2)	43 (4.4)	232 (3.3)
Hispanic		24 (2.9)	249 (4.4)	32 (4.7)	244 (3.1)	44 (3.6)	246 (2.2)
Asian/Pacific Islander		19 (4.7)	268 (6.7)	30 (6.8)	274 (7.3)	52 (9.4)	278 (5.8)
American Indian		13 (10.4)!	251 (18.9)!	64 (28.6)!	250 (18.2)!	23 (19.5)!	255 (8.2)!

		SCIENCE TEACHING EXPERIENCE					
		5 YEARS OR LESS EXPERIENCE		**MORE THAN 5 YEARS, LESS THAN 15 YEARS EXPERIENCE**		**15 YEARS OR MORE EXPERIENCE**	
	Avg. Yrs. Teaching	**Percent of Students**	**Average Proficiency**	**Percent of Students**	**Average Proficiency**	**Percent of Students**	**Average Proficiency**
Total	12 (0.5)	31 (2.6)	265 (2.5)	33 (3.5)	262 (2.1)	36 (3.0)	269 (1.9)
Male		29 (2.6)	266 (2.8)	34 (3.7)	265 (2.3)	36 (3.3)	272 (2.3)
Female		32 (2.8)	263 (3.0)	32 (3.4)	260 (2.3)	36 (3.0)	265 (1.9)
White		30 (3.0)	274 (2.5)	32 (4.1)	272 (2.5)	38 (3.7)	276 (1.8)
Black		36 (4.8)	233 (3.9)	34 (5.0)	232 (4.1)	30 (3.6)	235 (3.1)
Hispanic		30 (3.1)	250 (3.5)	38 (5.1)	244 (2.8)	33 (3.9)	244 (2.6)
Asian/Pacific Islander		23 (5.3)	269 (6.0)	32 (6.7)	271 (6.6)	45 (9.5)	280 (5.2)
American Indian		17 (11.9)!	255 (15.2)!	65 (26.4)!	250 (19.4)!	19 (15.7)!	254 (8.6)!

The standard errors of the estimated percentages and proficiencies appear in parentheses. It can be said with 95 percent certainty that for each population of interest, the value for the whole population is within plus or minus two standard errors of the estimate for the sample.

! Interpret with caution — the nature of the sample does not allow accurate determination of the variability of this estimated statistic.

The 1990 Science Report Card: NAEP's Assessment of Fourth, Eighth, and Twelfth Graders (National Center for Education Statistics, U.S. Department of Education, 1992).

of our nation's eighth graders were being taught by veteran teachers with more than 15 years of science teaching experience, nearly one-third were being taught science by teachers who had five or fewer years of science teaching experience. These percentages were generally similar across student gender and race/ethnicity subgroups.

There were no significant differences in the average science proficiency of students grouped by their teachers' years of overall teaching experience or years of science teaching experience. Such a result is not unexpected, since so many factors, in addition to teacher experience, may affect students' achievement in science.

LEVEL AND TYPE OF

TEACHING CERTIFICATION   TABLE 6.3 summarizes teachers' reports on their levels and types of teaching certification. Sixty-five percent of eighth-grade students were taught science by teachers who reported having the highest certification awarded by the state in which they taught; another 23 percent were taught by teachers with "regular" certification. The remaining 12 percent of the students were taught by teachers who were either not certified or had only provisional certification. Teachers were also asked if they were certified to teach particular areas, for example, middle school/ junior high school science. These results show that 88 percent of eighth graders were taught science by teachers who reported having certification in science at some grade level. There were no differences in average student proficiency when students were grouped by their teachers' reported level or type of certification. The lack of an apparent

TABLE 6.3
Eighth-Grade Science Teachers' Reports on Their Level and Type of Teaching Certification

	Percent of Students	Average Proficiency
Level of Certification		
None, Temporary, Probational, Provisional, or Emergency	12 (1.8)	264 (3.8)
Regular Certification, but not the Highest	23 (2.6)	261 (2.8)
Highest Certification (Permanent or Long-Term)	65 (2.5)	267 (1.8)
Type of Certification		
Elementary Education	32 (2.8)	263 (2.2)
Middle/Junior High Education	44 (3.6)	263 (2.2)
Elementary or Middle/Junior High Science, but not Secondary Science	74 (2.8)	264 (1.7)
Secondary, Junior High, or Elementary Science	88 (2.0)	265 (1.5)
No Science Certification	12 (2.0)	267 (3.6)

The standard errors of the estimated percentages and proficiencies appear in parentheses. It can be said with 95 percent certainty that for each population of interest, the value for the whole population is within plus or minus two standard errors of the estimate for the sample.

The 1990 Science Report Card: NAEP's Assessment of Fourth, Eighth, and Twelfth Graders (National Center for Education Statistics, U.S. Department of Education, 1992).

relationship between student science achievement and teacher certification may not be unusual considering that, in response to a 1987 survey conducted by the Council of Chief State School Officers, only 25 states reported specific certification requirements for the middle/junior high school level.[32] According to the survey results, 18 of these states reported that they required coursework in science and mathematics, with the amount required in each discipline ranging from 12 to 36 semester credit hours. Two states reported that they had no science coursework requirements at this level and an additional five states reported that the approved competency-based program or degree-granting institution sets certification standards.

ACADEMIC TRAINING   Eighth-grade science teachers' reports on their highest academic degree and type of undergraduate institution are shown in TABLE 6.4. Nearly half the eighth graders were taught science by teachers who had earned more than a bachelor's degree — in most cases, a master's degree. These teachers received their

TABLE 6.4
Eighth-Grade Science Teachers' Reports on Highest Academic Degree and Undergraduate Institution

	Percent of Students	Average Proficiency
Highest Academic Degree		
Bachelor's Degree	53 (2.8)	267 (1.6)
Master's or Specialist's Degree	47 (2.8)	264 (2.1)
Doctorate or Professional Degree	0 (0.2)	264 (8.8)
Type of Undergraduate Institution		
Teacher Training Institution	14 (2.1)	267 (2.9)
Liberal Arts College	27 (2.8)	262 (2.6)
Major Research University	27 (2.6)	267 (2.9)
Other College or University	31 (2.3)	267 (2.1)

The standard errors of the estimated percentages and proficiencies appear in parentheses. It can be said with 95 percent certainty that for each population of interest, the value for the whole population is within plus or minus two standard errors of the estimate for the sample. Percentages less than 0.5 percent were rounded to 0 percent.

The 1990 Science Report Card: NAEP's Assessment of Fourth, Eighth, and Twelfth Graders (National Center for Education Statistics, U.S. Department of Education, 1992).

[32] Rolf Blank, *State Education Policies on Science and Mathematics* (Washington, D.C.: Council of Chief State School Officers, 1987).

undergraduate degrees from a variety of institutions, primarily liberal arts colleges, major research universities, and other colleges or universities; 14 percent of eighth graders had science teachers who reported graduating from a teacher training institution. However, there were no significant differences in students' proficiency based on their teachers' highest academic degree or type of undergraduate institution.

Eighth-grade science teachers were asked to indicate the number of college courses they had completed in biology, chemistry, physics, and earth science. The results are shown in TABLE 6.5, along with the average science proficiency of those teachers' students. Ninety percent of eighth-grade students were taught science by teachers who had taken two or more college-level courses in biology, as compared to 68 percent who were taught by teachers who had taken two or more courses in chemistry, 62 percent by teachers who had taken two or more courses in earth science, and 54 percent by teachers who had taken two or more courses in physics. For each of these four subject areas, there were no significant differences in students' proficiency based on the amount of their teachers' college coursework. For example, the 7 percent of eighth graders taught by

TABLE 6.5
Eighth-Grade Science Teachers' Reports on the Number of Science Courses Taken as Part of Their Undergraduate and Graduate Study

	ONE OR NO COURSES		TWO OR THREE COURSES		FOUR OR FIVE COURSES		SIX OR MORE COURSES	
	% of Students	Avg. Profic.	% of Students	Avg. Profic.	% of Students	Avg. Profic.	% of Students	Avg. Profic.
Biology/ Life Sciences	10 (1.9)	269 (5.3)	19 (2.3)	264 (3.1)	14 (1.9)	271 (3.2)	57 (3.0)	264 (1.7)
Chemistry	32 (2.8)	265 (2.3)	31 (2.5)	268 (2.3)	21 (2.5)	263 (2.7)	16 (2.5)	263 (2.5)
Physics	46 (3.0)	266 (1.6)	38 (3.0)	265 (2.8)	9 (1.8)	263 (3.3)	7 (1.6)	266 (5.1)
Earth Sciences	37 (3.0)	263 (2.0)	25 (3.2)	265 (2.9)	10 (1.7)	268 (3.8)	27 (2.6)	268 (3.1)

The standard errors of the estimated percentages and proficiencies appear in parentheses. It can be said with 95 percent certainty that for each population of interest, the value for the whole population is within plus or minus two standard errors of the estimate for the sample.

The 1990 Science Report Card: NAEP's Assessment of Fourth, Eighth, and Twelfth Graders (National Center for Education Statistics, U.S. Department of Education, 1992).

teachers who had completed six or more physics courses had virtually the same proficiency as the 46 percent whose teachers had completed either one or no courses in physics.

According to the teachers' reports, the most common science course offerings at the eighth-grade level are earth science and physical science (see Chapter Five). Fifty-one percent of eighth graders were enrolled in a science course that emphasized earth science and 25 percent were enrolled in a course that emphasized physical science. A prime consideration is whether or not these students received instruction from teachers who have academic preparation in the science content areas that they were teaching. FIGURE 6.1 shows eighth-grade earth science teachers' reports on their college coursework in earth science and FIGURE 6.2 shows physical science teachers' reports on their college coursework in physical science. Eighty-two percent of eighth-grade earth science students were taught by teachers who had taken at least one course in earth science at the college level, most frequently physical geology and least frequently oceanography. Ninety-one percent of eighth-grade physical science students were taught by teachers who had taken at least one college-level course in physical science, most frequently general chemistry or general physics, and least frequently more specialized and advanced courses such as

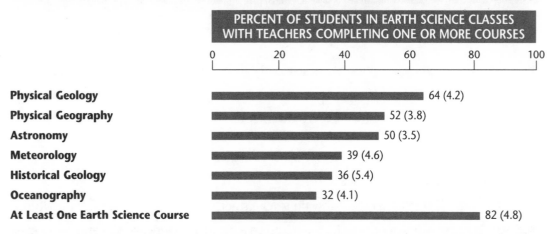

FIGURE 6.1
Eighth-Grade Earth Science Teachers' Reports on Their College Coursework in the Earth Sciences

PERCENT OF STUDENTS IN EARTH SCIENCE CLASSES WITH TEACHERS COMPLETING ONE OR MORE COURSES

Physical Geology	64 (4.2)
Physical Geography	52 (3.8)
Astronomy	50 (3.5)
Meteorology	39 (4.6)
Historical Geology	36 (5.4)
Oceanography	32 (4.1)
At Least One Earth Science Course	82 (4.8)

The standard errors of the estimated percentages appear in parentheses. It can be said with 95 percent certainty that for each population of interest, the value for the whole population is within plus or minus two standard errors of the estimate for the sample.

The 1990 Science Report Card: NAEP's Assessment of Fourth, Eighth, and Twelfth Graders (National Center for Education Statistics, U.S. Department of Education, 1992).

FIGURE 6.2
Eighth-Grade Physical Science Teachers' Reports on Their College Coursework in the Physical Sciences

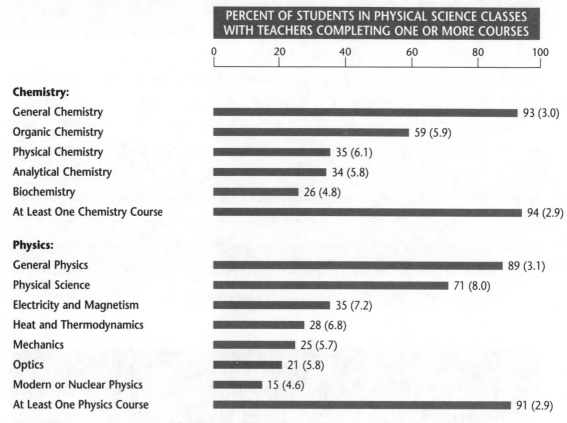

PERCENT OF STUDENTS IN PHYSICAL SCIENCE CLASSES WITH TEACHERS COMPLETING ONE OR MORE COURSES

Chemistry:
- General Chemistry — 93 (3.0)
- Organic Chemistry — 59 (5.9)
- Physical Chemistry — 35 (6.1)
- Analytical Chemistry — 34 (5.8)
- Biochemistry — 26 (4.8)
- At Least One Chemistry Course — 94 (2.9)

Physics:
- General Physics — 89 (3.1)
- Physical Science — 71 (8.0)
- Electricity and Magnetism — 35 (7.2)
- Heat and Thermodynamics — 28 (6.8)
- Mechanics — 25 (5.7)
- Optics — 21 (5.8)
- Modern or Nuclear Physics — 15 (4.6)
- At Least One Physics Course — 91 (2.9)

The standard errors of the estimated percentages appear in parentheses. It can be said with 95 percent certainty that for each population of interest, the value for the whole population is within plus or minus two standard errors of the estimate for the sample.

The 1990 Science Report Card: NAEP's Assessment of Fourth, Eighth, and Twelfth Graders (National Center for Education Statistics, U.S. Department of Education, 1992).

biochemistry, mechanics, optics, and nuclear physics. However, if as described in Chapter Five, a "less is more" approach to school science that requires an in-depth understanding of a few major concepts is desirable, then current levels of teacher training may be a concern.

TEACHERS' PERCEPTIONS OF THEIR PREPARATION TO TEACH

SCIENCE TOPICS   How do teachers perceive their preparation for teaching science? Eighth-grade science teachers were given a list of 19 science topics and asked to indicate how well prepared they felt to teach each one at the middle or junior high school level, regardless of whether they were currently teaching each topic. Response options were: "Well-prepared," e.g., would feel confident teaching topic; "Somewhat-prepared," e.g., would have to depend heavily on instructional resources; and "Ill-prepared," e.g., would find it difficult to teach even with resources. As shown in TABLE 6.6, percentages of students whose teachers felt well-prepared in particular physical science topics ranged from a low of 44 percent for electricity and magnetism to a high of 84 percent for properties of solids, liquids, and gases. Within the life sciences, 71 percent of students had teachers who felt well-prepared to teach cell structure and function, compared to approximately 50 percent that had teachers who felt well-prepared to teach classification schemes or the gene theory of heredity. There was little variation in the percentages of students whose teachers felt well-prepared to teach the various earth science topics included in the survey.

TABLE 6.6 also shows the percentages of students in life, physical, and earth science classes whose teachers felt well-prepared to teach the specific topics pertinent to each of those three types of eighth-grade science classes. Interestingly, most students in earth science classes had teachers who reported feeling well-prepared to teach each of the earth science topics included in the survey, even though many of these teachers did not report college coursework in some of the specific topic areas. For example, while only 39 percent of earth science students were taught by teachers who reported taking a college course in meteorology (see FIGURE 6.1), 84 percent had teachers who indicated feeling well-prepared to teach about weather and climate. Similarly, while only 35 percent of eighth-grade physical science students were taught by teachers who had taken at least one course in electricity and magnetism, 68 percent had teachers who reported feeling well-prepared to teach this topic. Perhaps teachers who feel well-prepared to teach topics in which they have not had a formal academic course are gaining preparation for teaching these topics from their more general introductory courses and from their experiences and in-service courses beyond college.

TEACHERS' PROFESSIONAL ACTIVITIES

IN SCIENCE
In-service education provides an opportunity for science teachers to remedy any inadequacies they might have had in their pre-service preparation as well as to stay abreast of the many rapid changes in science. However, as summarized in TABLE 6.7, only 13 percent of the nation's eighth-grade students had science teachers who reported spending more than 35 hours in the year preceding the 1990 assessment enrolled in workshops and courses related to science or science teaching. More than one-fourth of the eighth graders had teachers who did not participate in any in-service education in science. Approximately one-third of the students were taught by teachers who reported having attended a national or state science teacher association meeting during the last

TABLE 6.6
Eighth-Grade Science Teachers' Reports on Their Preparation to Teach Topics in Life, Physical, and Earth and Space Science

	PERCENT OF STUDENTS WHOSE TEACHERS CONSIDERED THEMSELVES WELL-PREPARED	
	All Students	**Students in Life Science Classes**
Life Science Topics		
Cell structure and function	71 (2.7)	90 (4.6)
Energy flow and food webs	66 (2.6)	75 (8.3)
Natural selection	64 (2.6)	79 (6.8)
Structure/function of organisms	64 (2.5)	87 (5.7)
Photosynthesis/cellular metabolism	60 (3.0)	77 (8.2)
Animal behavior	56 (3.2)	79 (6.8)
Gene theory of heredity	50 (2.5)	75 (8.7)
Classification schemes	48 (2.4)	66 (11.4)
	All Students	**Students in Physical Science Classes**
Physical Science Topics		
Properties of solids, liquids, gases	84 (1.6)	94 (1.7)
Periodic table of elements	77 (2.0)	85 (4.0)
Explaining the motion of objects	56 (3.3)	77 (4.3)
Waves (light and sound)	55 (3.1)	72 (5.4)
Kinetic theory of matter	50 (2.6)	72 (5.9)
Electricity and magnetism	44 (3.3)	68 (6.4)
	All Students	**Students in Earth Science Classes**
Earth and Space Science Topics		
The solar system	72 (2.8)	83 (3.7)
Weather and climate	70 (3.1)	84 (2.7)
Earth in space and time	67 (2.3)	81 (3.6)
The rock cycle	67 (2.5)	83 (2.7)
Plate tectonics	64 (2.9)	82 (3.1)

The standard errors of the estimated percentages appear in parentheses. It can be said with 95 percent certainty that for each population of interest, the value for the whole population is within plus or minus two standard errors of the estimate for the sample.

The 1990 Science Report Card: NAEP's Assessment of Fourth, Eighth, and Twelfth Graders (National Center for Education Statistics, U.S. Department of Education, 1992).

TABLE 6.7
Eighth-Grade Science Teachers' Reports on Professional Activities during the Past Year

	Percent of Students	Average Proficiency
Time Spent in Workshops or Courses Related to Science/Science Teaching		
None	27 (2.8)	265 (2.7)
Less Than 6 Hours	22 (2.7)	267 (2.6)
6 to 15 Hours	22 (2.7)	263 (2.0)
16 to 35 Hours	16 (2.2)	264 (3.5)
More Than 35 Hours	13 (1.9)	268 (3.2)
Taught Science In-Service Workshops or Courses		
Yes	11 (1.6)	263 (3.4)
No	90 (1.6)	266 (1.4)
Attended State/National Science Teacher Association Meetings		
Yes	33 (3.1)	265 (2.3)
No	67 (3.1)	265 (1.5)

The standard errors of the estimated percentages and proficiencies appear in parentheses. It can be said with 95 percent certainty that for each population of interest, the value for the whole population is within plus or minus two standard errors of the estimate for the sample.

The 1990 Science Report Card: NAEP's Assessment of Fourth, Eighth, and Twelfth Graders (National Center for Education Statistics, U.S. Department of Education, 1992).

year and about one in ten had teachers who served as instructors of in-service offerings for other science teachers.

SUMMARY   Most of the nation's eighth-grade students were taught science by teachers who had the highest certification awarded by the state in which they taught, were certified to teach science at some grade level, had at least a bachelor's degree, and received their undergraduate training from a four-year institution. Eighth graders were taught science by teachers who had been teaching for an average of 14 years and had been teaching science for an average of 12 years.

Ninety-one percent of the nation's eighth-grade physical science students were taught by teachers who had completed at least one college-level course in some aspect of physical science and 82 percent of eighth-grade earth science students were taught by teachers who had at least one college-level course in earth science. Most eighth graders

113

were taught by teachers who reported feeling well-prepared to teach the topics in their science classes. However, only a small percentage of eighth graders had teachers who participated in more than fifteen hours of in-service workshops, had taught an in-service workshop, or attended a national or state science teachers' association meeting during the year preceding the 1990 science assessment.

To provide a coherent perspective for the 1990 NAEP science results, we have attempted to place the findings in the context of the recommendations for science reform as articulated by the series of landmark reports published during the last decade. For example, increasing societal and school support for science education, emphasizing scientific literacy for all Americans, revamping the curriculum to include more in-depth study of central science concepts, and updating instructional approaches so that they are more reflective of the nature of science are consistent foci of publications referenced throughout this report. These substantial works produced by major stakeholders in improving science education, including the American Association for the Advancement of Science, the National Science Foundation, the National Academy of Science, and the National Science Teachers Association, tend also to stress the need for a well-trained, competent teaching force. For example, *Time for Results: The Governors' 1991 Report on Education* urged Americans to create a more professional teaching force,[33] Project 2061 has stressed the centrality of teachers in the reform movement,[34] and the National Science Board Commission placed top priority on retraining present teachers and recruiting science, technology, and mathematics teachers so that they would all be of high quality.[35]

In preceding chapters, the NAEP data revealed the relatively low priority given to science by schools, the low amount of science instruction in elementary schools, the pattern of high school students opting out of the science pipeline, teachers' tendency to rely on textbooks and lectures rather than on doing science in science classes, and the low science achievement for large segments of our nation's students. This chapter revealed that about one-third of the eighth graders were taught by teachers who had taken one or fewer courses in chemistry, and that about half were taught by teachers with an equally low amount of coursework in physics or the earth sciences, despite the fact that more than half of the students were in earth science courses and one-fourth were in courses related to the physical sciences. When teachers' backgrounds were matched to the classes they were

[33] *Time for Results: The Governors' 1991 Report on Education* (Washington, D.C.: National Governors' Association, 1991).

[34] *Science for All Americans: A Project 2061 Report on Literacy in Science, Mathematics, and Technology* (Washington, D.C.: American Association for the Advancement of Science, 1989).

[35] *Educating Americans for the 21st Century: A Report to the American People and the National Science Board* (Washington, D.C.: National Science Board Commission on Precollege Education in Mathematics, Science, and Technology, 1983).

teaching, the picture improved somewhat; yet nearly 20 percent of the eighth graders in earth science classes had teachers with no coursework in the subject and about 10 percent of those in physical science classes had teachers with no physics coursework.

According to teachers' reports, about 10 to 30 percent of the eighth graders were being taught topics in life, physical, and earth science by teachers who did not feel well-prepared to teach these topics. Conversely, considering the relatively low amount of college coursework reported by the teachers as well as the finding that about half of the students had teachers with less than six hours of in-service training during the year preceding the assessment, it is curious that so many teachers reported feeling well-prepared to teach the large variety of science topics listed. Is it that these teachers have mastered the eighth-grade textbooks or is it, as the studies of science reform suggest, that the teachers may be matching the content of their classes to their own low levels of science understanding?

APPENDIX A

OVERVIEW OF PROCEDURES USED IN THE 1990 SCIENCE ASSESSMENT

*T*his Appendix is intended to provide further information about the methods and procedures used in NAEP's 1990 science assessment. The forthcoming *NAEP 1990 Technical Report* provides more extensive information about procedures.

NAEP'S 1990 SCIENCE ASSESSMENT   The objectives for the 1990 NAEP science assessment were developed by an Assessment Development Panel, which included representatives from national science organizations, state departments of education, and local schools. An Item Development Panel of scientists and science educators developed and reviewed the items for the 1990 assessment using the framework provided in the objectives. The objectives for the 1990 assessment reflected three basic elements of scientific literacy: science knowledge, scientific habits of mind, and the ability to solve problems and conduct inquiries.[1]

Science knowledge embraces information not only about the natural phenomena that are the objects of study in the major scientific disciplines, but also about the fundamental concepts, principles, and theories in these disciplines. Additionally, students were expected to be informed about the nature of science, including a recognition of its characteristics, such as empirical and theoretical methods and philosophy that distinguish science from other human activities.

Scientific habits of mind pertain to students' ability to think scientifically and the inclination to do so beyond the confines of the science classroom. Creative thinking, inductive and deductive reasoning, and verbal, analogical, and spatial reasoning are among the primary aspects of scientific thinking. Yet the propensity to apply these habits of mind outside the science classroom depends not only on abilities but also on attitudes toward science and its relevance to life, views influenced both by experiences in school science and by personal variables, such as individual motivation and out-of-school involvement in science-related learning.

Solving problems and conducting inquiries encompass a wide range of activities, from the novice efforts of students interacting with the natural world to the work of experienced scientists. Science educators consider the students' capacity to employ these skills in various contexts as particularly indicative of science achievement.[2]

Using these elements of scientific literacy as a foundation, the Assessment Development Panel constructed the framework for the 1990 science assessment as a two-dimensional matrix —

---

[1] *Science Objectives: 1990 Assessment* (Princeton, NJ: National Assessment of Educational Progress, Educational Testing Service, 1990).

[2] Senta Raizen, et al., *Assessment in Science Education: the Middle Years* (Washington, D.C.: The National Center for Improving Science Education, 1991).

Content Areas by Thinking Skills — as presented in FIGURE A.1. *Thinking Skills* cover a range of knowledge and cognitive abilities that allow the scientifically literate individual to conduct inquiries and solve problems in various science content areas. *Content Areas* are the three traditional scientific disciplines — Life, Physical, and Earth and Space Sciences — to which thinking skills and the understanding of the nature of science are applied. The Nature of Science represents the understanding of the methods and processes of science, the principles underlying scientific work, and the nature of scientific knowledge.

FIGURE A.1
Framework for the 1992 Assessment

CONTENT AREAS

		Life Sciences	Physical Sciences	Earth & Space Sciences
	Conducting Inquiries			
THINKING SKILLS	Solving Problems			
	Knowing Science			
	NATURE OF SCIENCE			

The 1990 Science Report Card: NAEP's Assessment of Fourth, Eighth, and Twelfth Graders (National Center for Education Statistics, U.S. Department of Education, 1992).

To guide the development of assessment items, the panel assigned weights to each of the major categories in the framework, reflecting the relative importance of each of the content areas and thinking skills at each grade level. These percentages are presented in Tables A.1 and A.2. Each question in the assessment was classified into a cell of the framework matrix, matching the content area and thinking skill it was intended to measure. The design of the 1990 assessment thus allowed NAEP not only to report on average science proficiency for the nation and for population subgroups, but also to document students' performance on four subscales — life sciences, physical sciences, earth and space sciences, and the nature of science.

The 1990 science assessment contained 112 questions at grade 4, with 17 of them requiring students to construct their responses. At grade 8, there were 146 questions, 24 of which were constructed-response. Similarly, twelfth graders were administered a total of 150 questions, 24 of which were constructed-response. Of the constructed-response questions, about two-thirds were "figural response" questions, which required students to mark or draw responses to indicate direction, location, or arrangement of objects and to interpret and graph data.[3] The remaining constructed-response questions asked for essays or brief written responses.

THE ASSESSMENT DESIGN

Each student received a booklet containing a set of general background questions, a set of subject-specific background questions, and three 15-minute segments or blocks of cognitive items. At each grade level, the science assessment included seven different blocks of multiple-choice and constructed-response content questions. Students

[3] Michael Martinez, *A Comparison of Multiple-choice and Constructed Figural Response Items, Research Report 90-19* (Princeton, NJ: Educational Testing Service, 1990).

TABLE A.1
Percentage Distribution of Questions by Grade and Content Area

Content Area	Grade 4	Grade 8	Grade 12
Life Sciences	30	30	32
Physical Sciences	30	30	34*
Earth and Space Sciences	30	30	22
Nature of Science	10	10	12

* At grade 12, the Physical Sciences category includes approximately 17 percent chemistry and 17 percent physics questions.

The 1990 Science Report Card: NAEP's Assessment of Fourth, Eighth, and Twelfth Graders (National Center for Education Statistics, U.S. Department of Education, 1992).

TABLE A.2
Percentage Distribution of Questions by Grade and Thinking Skills

Thinking Skills	Grade 4	Grade 8	Grade 12
Knowing Science	40	40	40
Solving Problems	40	40	40
Conducting Inquiries	20	20	20

The 1990 Science Report Card: NAEP's Assessment of Fourth, Eighth, and Twelfth Graders (National Center for Education Statistics, U.S. Department of Education, 1992).

received different blocks of cognitive items in their booklets according to a careful plan. The 1990 assessment was based on an adaptation of matrix sampling called balanced incomplete block (BIB) spiraling — a design that enables broad coverage of science content while minimizing the burden for any one student. The balanced incomplete block part of the design assigns blocks of items to booklets, and each pair of blocks appears together in at least one booklet. The spiraling part of the design cycles the booklets for administration, so that typically only a few students in any assessment session receive the same booklet. In accordance with this design, the seven blocks were presented in seven booklets. Each block appeared in exactly three booklets, and each block appeared with every other block in at least one booklet.

At each grade, each booklet included two student background questionnaires. The first, consisting of general background questions, included questions about race/ethnicity, mother's and father's level of education, reading materials in the home, homework, attendance, academic expectations, and which parents live at home. The second, consisting of science background questions, included questions about instructional activities, courses taken, use of specialized resources such as science laboratory equipment, and attitudes about science. Students were given five minutes to complete each questionnaire, with the exception of the fourth graders who were allotted more time because the items in the general questionnaire were read aloud for them.

QUESTIONNAIRES   As part of the 1990 science assessment, questionnaires were given to the science teachers of the eighth-grade students participating in the assessment and to the principal or other administrator in each participating school at all three grades assessed. An expert panel developed guidelines for the school and teacher questionnaires focusing on six educational areas: curriculum, instructional practices, teacher qualifications, educational standards and reform, school conditions, and conditions outside of school that facilitate learning and instruction.[4] Similar to the development of the materials given to students, the policy guidelines and the teacher and school questionnaires were prepared through an iterative process that involved extensive development, field testing, and review by external advisory groups.

The questionnaire for eighth-grade science teachers was made possible by support from the National Science Foundation through a subcontract to Educational Testing Service from Horizon Research, Inc. The questionnaire consisted of two parts. The first requested information about the teacher, such as race/ethnicity and gender as well as academic degrees held, teaching certification, training in science, and ability to get instructional resources. In the second part, teachers were asked to provide information on each class they taught that included one or more students who participated in the assessment. The information included, among other things, the amount of time spent on science instruction and homework, the adequacy of classroom science equipment, the instructional emphasis placed on different science topics, and the use of various instructional approaches. Because the analysis of the questionnaire data was linked to participating students, the responses to the science teacher questionnaire as presented in this report reflect the population of students rather than the population of teachers.

The extensive school questionnaire completed by principals or other administrators in the participating schools contained questions about the individuals completing the questionnaire, school policies, course offerings, and special priority areas and resources, among other topics.

It is important to note that in this report, as in all NAEP reports, the student is always the unit of analysis, even when information from the teacher or school questionnaire is being reported. The alternatives are either to give additional weight to schools and teachers in proportion to the numbers of students that they influence, as was done in this report, or essentially to weight each teacher or school response equally as would be done, for example, to examine characteristics of schools across the nation regardless of their size. Using the student as the unit of analysis makes it possible to describe the instruction received by representative samples of students. Although this approach may provide a different perspective from that obtained by simply analyzing the information from teachers or schools to reflect those population results, it is consistent with NAEP's goal of providing information about the educational context and performance of students. However, as part of the Horizon Research, Inc. teacher questionnaire study, the results for the eighth-grade teachers were analyzed both as presented in this report and by using the teacher as the unit of analysis. Comparative data for the two perspectives will be provided in a forthcoming report.

AND DATA COLLECTION   Sampling and data collection activities for the 1990 NAEP assessment were conducted by Westat, Inc. As with all NAEP national assessments, the results are based on a stratified, three-stage sampling plan. The first stage included defining geographic primary sampling units (PSUs), which are typically groups of contiguous counties, but sometimes a single county; classifying the PSUs into strata defined by region and community type; and randomly selecting PSUs. For each grade, the second stage included listing, classifying, and randomly selecting schools, both public and private, within each PSU selected at the first stage. The third stage involved randomly selecting students within a school for participation. Some students that were selected (fewer than 6 percent) were excluded because of limited English proficiency or severe disability. In 1984, NAEP began collecting descriptive information on these excluded students in order to describe this group more fully. Further information about excluded students is available in the *NAEP 1990 Technical Report*.

[4] *National Assessment of Educational Progress, 1990 Background Questionnaire Framework* (Princeton, NJ: National Assessment of Educational Progress, Educational Testing Service, 1989).

The data collection was accomplished by members of Westat's field staff, who were thoroughly trained in NAEP procedures. The sample at each grade consisted of two equivalent half samples. The assessment was administered to the first half sample in the January to mid-March time frame, while it was administered to the second half sample in the mid-March to mid-May time frame.

TABLE A.3 presents the students and school sample sizes and the cooperation and response rates that provide the basis for this report.

TABLE A.3
Student and School Sample Sizes, 1990

Grade	Number of Students	Number of Participating Schools	Percent of Schools Participating	Percent of Student Completion
4	6,314	527	88.3	92.9
8	6,531	406	86.7	89.1
12	6,337	304	81.3	81.3
Total	19,182	1,237		

The 1990 Science Report Card: NAEP's Assessment of Fourth, Eighth, and Twelfth Graders (National Center for Education Statistics, U.S. Department of Education, 1992).

Although sampled schools that refused to participate were occasionally replaced, school cooperation rates were computed based on the schools originally selected for participation in the assessments. The rates, which are based on schools sampled for all subjects assessed in 1990 (reading, science, and mathematics), are also the best estimates for the science assessment. Of the participating schools, 790 were public schools, and 447 were Catholic and other private schools.

SCORING Materials from the 1990 assessment were shipped to National Computer Systems in Iowa City for processing. Receipt and quality control were managed through a sophisticated bar-coding and tracking system. After all appropriate materials were received from a school, they were forwarded to the professional scoring area, where the responses to the constructed-response items were evaluated by a trained staff using guidelines prepared by NAEP. Each question requiring students to write, draw, or provide information had a unique scoring guide that defined the criteria to be used in evaluating students' responses. For the science assessment, approximately 325,000 student responses were scored, including a 20 percent reliability sample. The overall percentage of exact agreement was 91 percent. Subsequent to the professional scoring, the booklets were scanned, and all information was transcribed to the NAEP database at ETS. Each processing activity was conducted with rigorous quality control.

*DATA ANALYSIS
AND IRT SCALING*   After the assessment information had been compiled in the
database, the data were weighted according to the population structure. The weighting reflected the
probability of selection for each student as a result of the sampling design, adjusted for
nonresponse. Through poststratification, the weighting assured that the representation of certain
subpopulations corresponded to figures from the U.S. Census and the Current Population Survey.[5]

Analyses were then conducted to determine the percentages of students who gave various
responses to each cognitive and background question. Item response theory (IRT) was used to
estimate average proficiency for the nation and various subgroups of interest within the nation.

IRT models the probability of answering an item correctly as a mathematical function of
proficiency or skill. The main purpose of IRT analysis is to provide a common scale on which
performance can be compared across groups, such as those defined by grades and subgroups, such
as those defined by race/ethnicity or gender. Because of the BIB spiraling design used by NAEP,
students do not receive enough questions about a specific topic to provide reliable information
about individual performance. Traditional test scores for individual students, even those based on
IRT, would lead to misleading estimates of population characteristics, such as subgroup means and
percentages of students at or above a certain proficiency level. Instead, NAEP constructs sets of
plausible values designed to represent the distribution of proficiency in the population. A plausible
value for an individual is not a scale score for that individual but may be regarded as a representative value from the distribution of potential scale scores for all students in the population with
similar characteristics and identical patterns of item response. Statistics describing performance on
the NAEP proficiency scale are based on these plausible values. They estimate values that would
have been obtained had individual proficiencies been observed — that is, had each student
responded to a sufficient number of cognitive items so that proficiency could be precisely
estimated.[6]

For the 1990 science assessment, NAEP created four IRT proficiency scales ranging from 0
to 500 for each of the four content areas specified in the framework — and an overall science
proficiency scale based on a composite of the content area scales, weighted to reflect the distributions shown previously in TABLE A.1.

As described earlier, the NAEP proficiency scales make it possible to examine relationships
between students' performance and a variety of background factors measured by NAEP. The fact
that a relationship exists between achievement and another variable, however, does not reveal the
underlying cause of the relationship, which may be influenced by a number of other variables.
Similarly, the assessments do not capture the influence of unmeasured variables. The results are
most useful when they are considered in combination with other knowledge about the student
population and the educational system, such as trends in instruction, changes in the school-age
population, and societal demands and expectations.

NAEP REPORTING GROUPS   This report contains results for the nation and
groups of students within the nation defined by shared characteristics. The definitions for subgroups as defined by race/ethnicity, size and type of community, parents' education level, gender,
and region follow:

RACE/ETHNICITY.   Results are presented for students of different racial/ethnic groups based
on the students' self-identification of race/ethnicity according to the following mutually exclusive
categories: White, Black, Hispanic, Asian/Pacific Islander, and American Indian (including Alaskan
Native). Some racial/ethnic group results are not reported for background variables, because this

---

[5] For additional information about the use of weighting procedures in NAEP, see Eugene G. Johnson, "Considerations and Techniques for the Analysis of NAEP Data," *Journal of Educational Statistics* 14:303-334, 1989.

[6] For theoretical justification of the procedures employed, see Robert J. Mislevy, "Randomization-based
Inferences About Latent Variables from Complex Samples," *Psychometrika* 56:177-196, 1991.

For computational details, see *Expanding the New Design: NAEP 1985-86 Technical Report* (Princeton, NJ:
Educational Testing Service, National Assessment of Education Progress, 1988) and the *1990 NAEP Technical
Report.*

further breakdown results in too few students. However, the data for all students, regardless of whether their racial/ethnic group was reported separately, were included in computing the overall national results.

TYPE OF COMMUNITY.   Results are provided for four mutually exclusive community types — advantaged urban, disadvantaged urban, extreme rural, and other — as described below.

Advantaged Urban: Students in this group reside in metropolitan statistical areas and attend schools where a high proportion of the students' parents are in professional or managerial positions.

Disadvantaged Urban: Students in this group reside in metropolitan statistical areas and attend schools where a high proportion of the students' parents are on welfare or are not regularly employed.

Extreme Rural: Students in this group do not reside in metropolitan statistical areas. They attend schools in areas with a population below 10,000 where many of the students' parents are farmers or farm workers.

Other: Students in the "Other" category attend schools in areas other than those defined as advantaged urban, disadvantaged urban, or extreme rural.

The information about parents' occupation was obtained from the Principal's Question-naire completed by each sampled school.

PARENTS' EDUCATION LEVEL.   Students were asked to indicate the extent of schooling for each of their parents — did not finish high school, graduated from high school, had some education after high school, or graduated from college. The response indicating the higher level of education for either parent was selected for reporting.

GENDER.   Results are reported separately for males and females. Gender was reported by the student.

REGION.   The United States has been divided into four regions: Northeast, Southeast, Central and West. States in each region are shown on the following map.

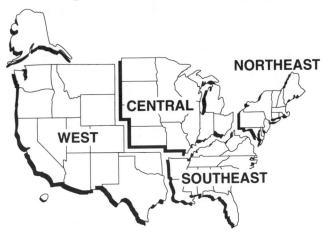

E S T I M A T I N G   V A R I A B I L I T Y   Because the statistics presented in this report are estimates of group and subgroup performance based on samples of students, rather than the values that could be calculated if every student in the nation answered every question, it is important to have measures of the degree of uncertainty of the estimates. Two components of uncertainty are accounted for in the variability of statistics based on proficiency: the uncertainty due to sampling only a relatively small number of students and the uncertainty due to sampling only a relatively small number of science questions. Because NAEP uses complex sampling procedures, conventional formulas for estimating sampling variability that assume simple random sampling are inappropri-ate. Consequently, NAEP uses a jackknife replication procedure to estimate standard errors. The jackknife standard error provides a reasonable measure of uncertainty for any information about students that can be observed without error, such as the percentages of students with a certain background characteristic or the percentage answering a question correctly. However, each student typically responds to so few items within any content area that the proficiency measurement for

123

any single student would be imprecise. In this case, using plausible values technology makes it possible to describe the performance of groups and subgroups of students, but the underlying imprecision that makes this step necessary adds an additional component of variability to statistics based on NAEP proficiencies.[7]

The standard errors for means and proportions reported by NAEP are statistics and subject to a certain degree of uncertainty. In certain cases, typically when the standard error is based on a small number of students or when the group of students is enrolled in a small number of schools, the amount of uncertainty associated with the standard errors may be quite large. Throughout this report, estimates of standard errors subject to a large degree of uncertainty are designated by the symbol "!". In such cases, the standard errors — and any confidence intervals or significance tests involving these standard errors — should be interpreted cautiously.

DRAWING INFERENCES FROM THE RESULTS

The use of *confidence intervals*, based on the standard errors, provides a way to make inferences about the population means and proportions in a manner that reflects the uncertainty associated with the sample estimates. An estimated sample mean proficiency ± 2 standard errors represents an approximate 95 *percent confidence interval* for the corresponding population quantity. This means that with approximately 95 percent certainty, the sample mean is within ± 2 standard errors of the average performance of the entire population of interest.

As an example, suppose that the average science proficiency of students in a particular group was 256, with a standard error of 1.2. A 95 percent confidence interval for the population quantity would be as follows:

$$\text{Mean} \pm 2 \text{ standard errors} = 256 \pm 2 \bullet (1.2) = 256 \pm 2.4 =$$
$$256 - 2.4 \text{ and } 256 + 2.4 = 253.6, 258.4$$

Thus, a 95 percent confidence interval for the average proficiency for the entire population of students in that group is 253.6 to 258.4.

Similar confidence intervals can be constructed for percentages, *provided that the percentages are not extremely large (greater than 90) or extremely small (less than 10)*. For extreme percentages, confidence intervals constructed in the above manner may not be appropriate and procedures for obtaining accurate confidence intervals are quite complicated.

To determine whether there is a *real difference* between the mean proficiency (or proportion of a certain attribute) for *two groups* in the population, one needs to obtain an estimate of the degree of uncertainty associated with the difference between the proficiency means or proportions of these groups for the sample. This estimate of the degree of uncertainty — called *the standard error of the difference* between the groups — is obtained by taking the square of each group's standard error, summing these squared standard errors, and then taking the square root of this sum.

Similar to the manner in which the standard error for an individual group mean or proportion is used, the *standard error of the difference* can be used to help determine whether differences between groups in the population are real. The difference between the mean proficiency or proportion of the two groups ± 2 *standard errors of the difference* represents an approximate 95 percent confidence interval. If the resulting interval includes zero, one should conclude that there is insufficient evidence to claim a real difference between groups in the population. If the interval does not contain zero, the difference between groups is *statistically significant* (different) at the .05 level.

The procedures described in this section, and the certainty ascribed to intervals (e.g., a 95 percent confidence interval), are based on statistical theory that assumes that only one confidence interval or test of statistical significance is being performed. When one considers sets of confidence intervals, like those at a grade level for all regions of the country or all five racial/ethnic groups defined by NAEP, statistical theory indicates that the certainty associated with the entire set of

[7] For further details, see Eugene G. Johnson, "Considerations and Techniques for the Analysis of NAEP Data", *Journal of Educational Statistics*, 14:303-334, 1989.

intervals is less than that attributable to each individual comparison from the set. If one wants to hold the certainty level for the set of comparisons at a particular level (e.g., .05), adjustments (called multiple comparison procedures) must be made. In other words, if many statistical tests are conducted at one time, it is likely that those tests will overstate the degree of statistical significance of the results. The problem arises because the more statistical tests are conducted, the more likely that one will find a "significant" finding because of chance variation. That is, the chance of a type I error — a spurious "significant" finding — rises with the number of tests conducted. Multiple-comparisons procedures are useful for controlling the overall type I error rate for a defined set — called a family — of hypothesis tests. For this report, the Hochberg stagewise Bonferroni procedure was used.[8] Multiple-comparison tests were performed for all pairs of means within the following families:

a) Marginal main effects for all reporting variables (e.g. a comparison of all six pairs of mean proficiencies for the four regions or comparisons of proportions of students in a series of subpopulations defined by some characteristic). Each reporting variable defines a separate family of the $n(n-1)/2$ possible comparisons between all pairs of the n categories of the variable.

b) Conditional main effects (e.g., comparisons of all pairs of regional means for males or for Hispanic students). These were computed for all reporting variables conditional on membership in categories of the following major reporting variables: gender, race/ethnicity, region, age, type of community, parents' education, and type of school.

c) Two way interactions (e.g., race by region) for all main reporting variables by all reporting variables. Each family of comparisons consists of all possible t-tests of the form

$$\{(Y_{ij} - Y_{ik}) - (Y_{hj} - Y_{hk})\}/(SE^2_{ij} + SE^2_{ik} + SE^2_{hj} + SE^2_{hk})^{1/2}$$

where i and h are two categories of one reporting variable and j and k are two categories of the other.

[8] Yosef Hochberg, "A Sharper Bonferroni Procedure for Multiple Tests of Significance", *Biometrika* 75:800-802, 1988.

APPENDIX B

*T*HE NAEP SCALE ANCHORING PROCESS FOR THE 1990 SCIENCE ASSESSMENT AND ADDITIONAL EXAMPLE ANCHOR ITEMS

INTRODUCTION   *I*n brief, NAEP's scale anchoring procedure was based on comparing item-level performance by students at four levels on the 0 to 500 overall science proficiency scale — Levels 200, 250, 300, and 350. Initially, this analysis was conducted on the 1986 science assessment results, and five sets of anchor items were delineated that discriminated between adjacent performance levels on the scale. The five sets of empirically derived anchor items, which also included a set of questions for level 150, were studied by a panel of science educators who carefully considered and articulated the types of knowledge, skills, and reasoning abilities demonstrated by correct responses to the items in each set of questions. This process was repeated, based on the 1990 science assessment results, and the descriptions were judged to still be valid with only slight revisions. The major difference was that the small number of items anchoring at Level 150 was insufficient to verify the 1986 description of performance at that level. Thus for this report, analyses are not presented for Level 150.

This appendix also contains the remaining anchor items available for public release, together with their performance results. Among other purposes, these items are presented in addition to those shown in Chapter Two to help provide further context and detail for the anchor level descriptions.

THE SCALE ANCHORING ANALYSIS   NAEP's scale anchoring procedure is grounded in an empirical process whereby the scaled assessment results are analyzed to delineate sets of items that discriminate between adjacent performance levels on the scale. For the 1990 science assessment, these levels were 200, 250, 300, and 350. For these four levels, items were identified that were likely to be answered correctly by students performing at a particular level on the scale and much less likely to be answered correctly by students performing at the next lower level. To provide a sufficient pool of respondents, students at Level 200 were defined as those whose estimated science proficiency was between 187.5 and 212.5; students at 250 were defined as those with estimated proficiency between 237.5 and 262.5; those at 300 had estimated proficiencies between 287.5 and 312.5; and those at 350 between 337.5 and 362.5. In theory, proficiency levels above 350 or below 200 could have been defined; however, so few students in the assessment performed at the extreme ends of the scale that it was not possible to do so.

The 1990 science scale anchoring analysis was based on the scaled proficiency results for fourth, eighth, and twelfth graders participating in the 1990 assessment. As illustrated here, ETS determined the weighted percentage and raw frequency for students at each of the four scale levels correctly answering each item. This was done for each of the grade levels at which the item was administered, and for the grade levels combined if the item was administered at more than one grade level. Regardless of the grade level, the data for each item were analyzed as shown in the following sample.

SAMPLE SCALE ANCHORING RESULTS

Scale Point	200	250	300	350
Weighted P-Value	0.32	0.66	0.92	0.97
Raw Frequency	1,247	2,142	1,430	391

The percentages of students answering the item correctly at the four scale levels differ from the overall p-value for the total sample at any one grade level, although the p-values for the total sample were also provided as part of the scale anchoring analysis.

Criteria were applied to the scale-level results, and an analysis was conducted to delineate the items that discriminated between scale levels. Because it was the lowest level being defined, Level 200 did not have to be analyzed in terms of the next lower level, but was examined for the percentage of students at that level answering the item correctly. More specifically, for an item to anchor at Level 200:

1) The p-value for students at Level 200 had to be greater than or equal to 0.65.

2) The calculation of the p-value at that level had to have been based on at least 100 students.

As an example:

LEVEL 200 ANCHOR ITEM RESULTS

Scale Point	200	250	300	350
Weighted P-Value	0.73	0.94	0.98	1.00
Raw Frequency	1,129	1,688	704	52

For an item to anchor at the remaining levels, additional criteria had to be met. For example, to anchor at Level 250:

1) The p-value for students at Level 250 had to be greater than or equal to 0.65.

2) The p-value for students at Level 200 had to be less than or equal to 0.50.

3) The difference between the two p-values had to be at least 0.30.

4) The calculations of the p-values at both levels 200 and 250 had to have been based on at least 100 students.

The following data set illustrates the results for a Level 250 anchor item:

LEVEL 250 ANCHOR ITEM RESULTS

Scale Point	200	250	300	350
Weighted P-Value	0.39	0.71	0.89	0.93
Raw Frequency	1,125	1,685	671	61

The same principles were used to identify anchor items at Levels 300 and 350:

1) The p-value at the anchor level had to be greater than or equal to 0.65.

2) The p-value at the adjacent lower level had to be less than or equal to 0.50.

3) The difference between the p-values had to be greater than or equal to 0.30.

4) The p-values at the adjacent levels being considered had to have been based on at least 100 students.

For example, the following results were obtained for an item anchoring at Level 300:

LEVEL 300 ANCHOR ITEM RESULTS

Scale Point	200	250	300	350
Weighted P-Value	0.27	0.43	0.76	.85
Raw Frequency	1,116	1,682	671	61

The results below are for an item anchoring at Level 350:

LEVEL 350 ANCHOR ITEM RESULTS

Scale Point	200	250	300	350
Weighted P-Value	0.13	0.16	0.43	0.85
Raw Frequency	430	1,377	1,369	399

For any given anchor item, the students at the anchor level are likely to answer the item correctly ($p \geq .65$), while the students at the next lower level are less likely to answer the item correctly ($p \leq .30$), and those at the next lower level are somewhat unlikely to answer the item correctly ($p \leq .50$). Collectively, as identified through this procedure, the 1990 NAEP science items at each anchor level represented advances in students' understandings from one level to the next — science areas where students at that level were more likely to answer items correctly than were students at the next lower level.

THE SCALE ANCHORING RESULTS   The 1990 analysis procedures yielded 7 questions that anchored at Level 200, 15 questions at Level 250, 34 questions at Level 300, and 10 questions at Level 350. To provide information for cross-referencing purposes, items that almost anchored were also identified. These items fulfilled all the criteria, but one of the p-values under consideration was less than 0.05 different from the criterion value. The items were arranged in the following order: anchored at 200, almost anchored at 200, anchored at 250, almost anchored at 250, anchored at 300, etc. Again, for further cross-referencing purposes, the remaining items in the assessment were also identified under the "did not anchor" heading. Each item was accompanied by its scoring guide (for constructed-response items) and by the full anchoring documentation which included anchoring information for each grade level at which an item was administered, the anchoring information across grades, the p-value for the total population of respondents at each grade level, and the science content area and thinking skill classifications. This arrangement facilitated the process of referencing the 1990 results against those obtained in 1986.

ADDITIONAL EXAMPLES OF ANCHOR ITEMS

EXAMPLE: LEVEL 200

Percent Correct for Anchor Levels

200	250	300	350
65	97	98	—

When you inhale, the air enters your

A stomach

(B) lungs

C heart

D liver

EXAMPLE: LEVEL 250

Percent Correct for Anchor Levels

200	250	300	350
36	76	91	—

Which of the following is NOT a fossil?

A An imprint of a leaf in a rock

B A fish skeleton in sandstone

(C) A quartz crystal

D A mastodon's tooth

EXAMPLE: LEVEL 250

Knowledge of Earth's past continues to change as scientists find additional fossils. This is because

A scientific knowledge cannot be trusted

B scientists change their ideas as new evidence is found

C scientists do not accurately report what they observe

D fossil study is not a true science

EXAMPLE: LEVEL 250

Which of the following statements about scientific knowledge is correct?

A It is based on observations and experiments that can be repeated by scientists.

B It cannot be tested.

C It is based on laws that never change.

D It is based on beliefs and faith.

EXAMPLE: LEVEL 300

Percent Correct for Anchor Levels			
200	250	300	350
19	48	83	—

Microscopes can be used to observe

A distant stars

B air temperature

C wind speed

D sand grains

EXAMPLE: LEVEL 300

Percent Correct for Anchor Levels			
200	250	300	350
26	36	69	—

Which of the following is the main cause of winds on Earth?

A Worldwide airline traffic

B Thunder and lightning storms

C Uneven heating of the surface of Earth

D Movement of the Moon around Earth

EXAMPLE: LEVEL 300

Percent Correct for Anchor Levels			
200	250	300	350
17	33	74	—

Which of the following should a science class do to find out which wind direction is most common during times of cloudy skies and wet weather in their town?

A Check a weathervane, thermometer, and barometer daily.

B Make a chart of the different cloud formations shown in an encyclopedia.

C Keep a record of daily rainfall for an entire year.

(D) Record wind direction, cloud conditions, and rainfall daily for at least 4 months.

EXAMPLE: LEVEL 300

The diagram below shows a thermometer. On the diagram, fill in the thermometer so that it reads 37.5 degrees Celsius (°C).

135

EXAMPLE: LEVEL 300

While she was watching a storm, Marie noticed that she always heard thunder shortly after she saw a flash of lightning. After 20 minutes, she found that the time between a flash of lightning and the sound of thunder was getting longer.

Which of the following statements best explains Marie's observations?

A The storm was moving closer to Marie.

(B) The storm was moving further from Marie.

C The storm was not moving.

D The storm was losing strength.

EXAMPLE: LEVEL 300

In the United States, each day the Sun rises in the

A north and sets in the south

B south and sets in the north

C west and sets in the east

(D) east and sets in the west

EXAMPLE: LEVEL 300

Which of the following is the best way to investigate the effect of fertilizers on potato plants?

A Put several plants outdoors and several indoors.

B Add fertilizer to several plants.

C Grow several plants under the same conditions but vary the amount of fertilizer added to each.

D Grow several plants under various temperature conditions.

EXAMPLE: LEVEL 300

A student observed a spider and its web. Which of the following is NOT an observation?

A The web has some threads that are straight.

B The spider has eight legs.

C The spider's abdomen is larger than its head.

D The spider makes no noise.

E The spider evolved from insects.

EXAMPLE: LEVEL 300

Hypotheses are

(A) ideas that can be tested

B facts about science

C observations of nature

D results of experiments

EXAMPLE: LEVEL 300

Measurements taken during a scientific experiment should be both accurate and precise. Accuracy refers to the

(A) closeness of the measurements to the true value

B reproducibility of the measurements

C location of the measurements taken

D time between measurements taken

E number of measurements taken

▶ **Questions 8–9** refer to an experiment in which moths were captured by attracting them to either white or yellow light. The results are shown in the graph below.

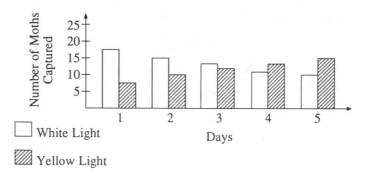

The graph shows that

A moths prefer yellow light

B only white moths are attracted to white light

C the number of moths captured per day using yellow light decreased after Day 5

D the number of moths captured per day using white light decreased during the experiment

139

EXAMPLE: LEVEL 300

A plant scientist is developing a new fertilizer, HYPERGROW. She designs an experiment to test whether HYPERGROW helps plants grow faster than does SUPERGROW, a fertilizer already on the market.

How should she apply fertilizer to the plants?

A Apply a mixture of SUPERGROW and HYPERGROW to the roots of all the plants.

B Apply a mixture of SUPERGROW and HYPERGROW to the growing tips of all the plants.

C Apply SUPERGROW to one-third of the plants, HYPERGROW to one-third of the plants, and nothing to the last third.

D Apply SUPERGROW to the leaves on the left side of each plant and HYPERGROW to the leaves on the right side of each plant.

EXAMPLE: LEVEL 300

Sugar Cubes   Loose Sugar

Two forms of sugar are shown above—solid cubes and packets of loose crystals. One cube has the same amount of sugar as one packet. Write your answers to the following questions in your **ANSWER BOOK.**

Which of the two forms of sugar dissolves faster in water?

Why?

Because it takes more time for the cube to loosen and start dissolving. The other sugar is already all-apart, so it can start dissolving right away.

141

EXAMPLE: LEVEL 350

Which of the following wears down the Earth's land surface the most?

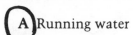 **A** Running water

B Earthquakes

C Volcanoes

D Wind

EXAMPLE: LEVEL 350

A plant scientist is developing a new fertilizer, HYPERGROW. She designs an experiment to test whether HYPERGROW helps plants grow faster than does SUPERGROW, a fertilizer already on the market.

Of the numbers below, which would be the number of plants the scientist could use to obtain the most reliable data?

A   1

B   2

C   20

D 200

EXAMPLE: LEVEL 350

Grade 12: 46% Correct Overall

Percent Correct for Anchor Levels

200	250	300	350
19	24	47	86

An object is hung on a string so that it can swing back and forth. To find out if the weight of an object affects the amount of time it takes to swing back and forth 10 times, which of the following should be changed for each timing measurement?

A The weight of the object

B The length of the swing

C The angle through which the object swings

D The distance the object swings

E The number of swings the object makes

EXAMPLE: LEVEL 350

Grade 4: 35% Correct Overall

Percent Correct for Anchor Levels

200	250	300	350
18	20	34	71

Strawberries appear to be red because red light

A is absorbed by them

B has a shorter wavelength than blue light

C reflects off them

D passes through them

E bends around them

143

EXAMPLE: LEVEL 350

Finding Relative Humidity (%)										
Dry Bulb Temperature (° C)	Difference Between Wet Bulb and Dry Bulb Temperatures (° C)									
	1	2	3	4	5	6	7	8	9	10
19	91	82	74	65	58	50	43	36	29	22
20	91	83	74	66	59	51	44	37	31	24
21	91	83	74	67	60	53	46	39	32	26
22	92	83	76	68	61	54	47	40	34	28
23	92	84	76	69	62	55	48	42	36	30
24	92	84	77	69	62	56	49	43	37	31

If the dry bulb temperature stays the same, and the difference between the dry bulb and wet bulb temperature increases, the relative humidity

A increases

B decreases

C stays the same

D cannot be determined

144

DATA APPENDIX

	MEAN	STD DEV	5TH	10TH	25TH	50TH	75TH	90TH	95TH
-- TOTAL --	232.8(0.9)	31.3(0.4)	179.4(1.3)	191.3(1.2)	211.6(1.1)	233.9(1.5)	254.9(1.2)	272.1(1.1)	282.0(1.4)
SEX									
MALE	233.8(1.1)	31.8(0.6)	179.5(2.1)	191.4(1.5)	211.9(1.3)	235.0(1.5)	256.6(1.2)	274.0(1.4)	284.3(1.7)
FEMALE	231.7(1.0)	30.6(0.6)	179.2(1.4)	191.0(1.2)	211.3(1.2)	232.9(0.9)	253.0(1.3)	269.9(1.0)	279.6(2.5)
RACE/ETHNICITY									
WHITE	242.1(1.0)	27.3(0.6)	195.5(1.7)	206.3(1.8)	224.2(1.6)	242.8(1.0)	261.1(1.1)	276.5(0.9)	286.2(1.0)
BLACK	205.4(1.5)	26.6(0.7)	162.3(1.8)	172.2(2.2)	187.9(2.3)	204.8(1.6)	222.6(1.4)	239.2(1.8)	251.1(2.3)
HISPANIC	212.0(1.5)	29.2(1.0)	163.4(2.4)	173.9(5.1)	192.3(1.7)	211.7(1.9)	231.4(0.9)	250.0(1.7)	260.9(3.3)
ASIAN/PACIFIC ISLANDER	233.2(3.0)	30.1(2.2)	186.1(4.2)	195.2(7.9)	212.3(3.1)	230.7(4.9)	253.1(6.8)	274.9(6.2)	286.9(6.4)
AMERICAN INDIAN/ ALASKAN NATIVE	226.1(2.7)	27.7(1.3)	180.5(6.9)	191.2(2.6)	207.0(6.2)	226.9(9.9)	245.8(4.5)	262.8(6.9)	270.1(4.9)
REGION									
NORTHEAST	235.6(1.9)	32.6(1.3)	178.3(4.2)	191.4(3.5)	214.1(2.8)	238.1(3.0)	258.8(2.3)	275.4(3.4)	285.9(2.5)
SOUTHEAST	226.7(2.3)	30.5(0.9)	176.8(3.3)	187.7(3.7)	205.3(2.3)	226.6(3.0)	248.0(2.4)	265.9(2.9)	276.8(3.8)
CENTRAL	234.3(2.2)	29.6(1.1)	182.7(2.7)	194.6(3.0)	215.2(3.2)	236.1(3.1)	254.8(2.5)	271.6(2.3)	280.1(2.8)
WEST	234.4(2.0)	31.7(1.0)	180.8(2.6)	192.3(2.4)	212.9(1.8)	235.6(2.1)	257.2(2.7)	274.1(2.0)	285.1(2.1)
TYPE OF COMMUNITY									
EXTREME RURAL	235.0(2.6)	27.4(1.1)	189.4(3.6)	199.0(4.5)	217.7(2.9)	235.1(4.2)	253.6(3.3)	270.4(1.8)	280.2(7.4)
DISADVANTAGED URBAN	208.6(2.6)	30.6(1.2)	159.1(3.8)	169.7(1.8)	187.0(3.0)	207.4(4.6)	230.1(4.6)	249.1(2.2)	260.0(6.5)
ADVANTAGED URBAN	251.6(2.4)	26.5(1.4)	204.7(8.7)	217.5(7.1)	235.9(2.4)	253.0(2.6)	269.6(2.0)	284.5(2.7)	292.4(3.6)
OTHER	232.6(1.0)	30.4(0.5)	181.5(1.3)	192.5(1.2)	211.8(1.1)	233.3(1.2)	253.9(1.5)	271.3(1.7)	281.1(1.0)
PARENTS' EDUCATION LEVEL									
LESS THAN H.S.	221.4(2.2)	27.9(1.5)	175.1(8.8)	185.1(4.6)	202.9(2.8)	222.0(2.7)	240.5(6.0)	258.1(6.1)	267.8(5.4)
GRADUATED H.S.	225.7(1.4)	28.9(0.8)	176.8(1.8)	188.3(2.0)	206.1(1.1)	226.4(1.6)	246.1(1.4)	262.9(2.0)	271.5(2.2)
SOME EDUCATION AFTER H.S.	241.9(1.8)	29.2(0.9)	187.9(3.6)	201.8(1.4)	223.7(3.9)	244.9(3.4)	262.4(1.8)	276.9(1.5)	284.8(3.6)
GRADUATED COLLEGE	242.7(1.2)	31.5(0.6)	186.8(2.0)	199.8(2.6)	221.9(2.1)	245.2(1.6)	265.5(1.1)	281.2(2.3)	290.6(1.1)
UNKNOWN	225.8(0.8)	29.4(0.6)	175.1(1.8)	187.4(2.9)	206.1(1.3)	227.2(0.9)	246.1(0.9)	262.5(2.4)	272.4(1.8)
TYPE OF SCHOOL									
PUBLIC	231.4(1.0)	31.4(0.5)	178.1(2.2)	190.0(1.1)	210.1(1.4)	232.5(1.3)	253.5(1.3)	271.1(1.2)	281.0(1.1)
PRIVATE	243.4(1.9)	28.1(0.9)	195.9(3.7)	206.3(3.4)	225.1(2.5)	244.4(1.9)	263.2(2.0)	278.6(4.1)	288.7(3.4)

The standard errors of the estimated proficiencies appear in parentheses. It can be said with 95 percent certainty that for each population of interest the value for the whole population is within plus or minus two standard errors of the estimate for the sample.

	MEAN	STD DEV	5TH	10TH	25TH	50TH	75TH	90TH	95TH
-- TOTAL --	263.1(1.2)	39.5(0.6)	195.3(2.2)	210.3(1.8)	236.6(1.4)	265.3(1.3)	291.0(1.5)	312.5(1.8)	324.4(2.2)
SEX									
MALE	265.1(1.6)	41.3(0.8)	195.1(2.2)	210.2(2.9)	237.0(1.8)	266.9(2.0)	294.9(2.4)	317.7(1.5)	329.8(1.0)
FEMALE	261.0(1.2)	37.6(0.6)	195.5(1.7)	210.5(1.7)	236.0(1.3)	263.8(1.5)	287.8(1.9)	306.9(1.4)	318.3(1.9)
RACE/ETHNICITY									
WHITE	272.9(1.4)	35.7(0.6)	211.5(2.4)	225.4(1.9)	249.0(1.7)	274.7(1.8)	297.9(1.6)	317.6(1.3)	329.1(2.1)
BLACK	231.0(2.2)	36.5(1.2)	171.9(6.8)	185.3(2.6)	205.7(2.4)	230.2(2.8)	257.3(3.1)	277.8(2.7)	288.9(2.6)
HISPANIC	241.2(2.1)	36.2(1.0)	180.6(1.9)	193.6(3.2)	216.4(3.8)	242.4(3.7)	266.3(1.9)	286.7(2.1)	299.7(2.7)
ASIAN/PACIFIC ISLANDER	270.5(4.0)	36.5(2.2)	207.4(10.4)	221.6(4.6)	246.1(7.4)	270.8(8.8)	297.2(5.0)	317.0(5.9)	327.1(4.6)
AMERICAN INDIAN/ ALASKAN NATIVE!	251.9(8.5)	35.3(3.0)	190.4(8.7)	207.4(11.4)	230.1(12.2)	253.1(13.3)	279.1(7.3)	295.5(6.7)	307.5(5.5)
REGION									
NORTHEAST	269.2(3.2)	39.1(1.7)	198.7(7.2)	216.9(6.5)	244.8(3.3)	272.3(2.9)	296.9(2.8)	317.0(3.1)	329.3(3.0)
SOUTHEAST	256.3(2.0)	39.1(1.0)	190.5(3.7)	204.4(3.7)	229.8(2.3)	258.1(2.1)	283.6(1.9)	305.9(1.8)	318.6(2.8)
CENTRAL	264.5(2.0)	38.9(1.0)	195.4(4.9)	211.2(3.9)	239.4(3.2)	267.8(2.8)	291.8(2.0)	312.5(3.2)	322.7(1.3)
WEST	263.1(2.8)	39.8(0.9)	197.1(2.8)	211.2(3.5)	235.5(2.9)	263.6(2.7)	292.0(4.2)	314.1(3.5)	327.1(4.5)
TYPE OF COMMUNITY									
EXTREME RURAL	257.4(3.2)	38.2(1.3)	195.6(4.4)	208.4(4.8)	231.3(3.6)	257.6(3.7)	283.5(3.9)	307.1(3.8)	320.1(3.8)
DISADVANTAGED URBAN	242.2(4.2)	41.1(1.6)	175.2(9.6)	189.8(3.4)	213.1(4.7)	243.1(4.6)	270.1(3.7)	295.8(4.3)	308.4(4.9)
ADVANTAGED URBAN!	283.4(4.1)	34.7(1.0)	223.0(5.1)	236.7(2.2)	260.7(4.9)	286.0(4.4)	307.5(3.7)	326.6(5.7)	337.7(5.6)
OTHER	263.7(1.5)	38.6(0.7)	196.8(3.1)	212.1(2.3)	237.8(1.7)	266.2(1.4)	290.8(1.6)	311.9(1.9)	323.5(2.2)
PARENTS' EDUCATION LEVEL									
LESS THAN H.S.	241.1(2.3)	33.7(1.4)	186.6(4.8)	197.8(5.2)	216.7(6.7)	242.1(5.7)	265.1(2.6)	283.3(2.3)	294.3(5.1)
GRADUATED H.S.	254.1(1.3)	36.7(1.0)	191.1(3.7)	205.0(2.3)	229.5(1.5)	256.2(1.2)	280.5(1.6)	299.9(1.6)	310.5(1.7)
SOME EDUCATION AFTER H.S.	268.4(1.4)	36.2(1.1)	205.0(7.7)	221.6(2.3)	246.5(2.0)	270.5(1.4)	293.1(2.0)	313.0(4.0)	324.2(5.4)
GRADUATED COLLEGE	276.4(1.7)	37.9(0.7)	209.3(2.4)	224.5(2.8)	251.6(2.7)	279.8(1.8)	303.5(1.7)	322.5(1.6)	333.7(2.5)
UNKNOWN	236.5(2.3)	38.3(1.4)	172.5(5.5)	186.3(6.0)	210.9(5.9)	236.9(4.1)	262.7(8.1)	285.8(7.5)	298.4(2.1)
TYPE OF SCHOOL									
PUBLIC	261.5(1.4)	39.8(0.6)	193.6(1.5)	208.3(2.0)	234.7(2.4)	263.5(1.4)	289.8(1.9)	311.8(1.9)	323.6(1.7)
PRIVATE	274.9(1.9)	34.7(1.2)	216.8(5.1)	228.6(5.5)	251.8(2.9)	276.6(3.8)	298.0(2.4)	318.6(2.6)	329.6(4.9)
ABILITY OF STUDENTS IN CLASS									
HIGH ABILITY	289.6(1.9)	33.5(1.4)	229.8(5.4)	245.4(5.0)	268.6(3.3)	291.7(2.7)	313.5(3.8)	331.8(2.5)	340.4(3.9)
AVERAGE ABILITY	266.5(1.4)	35.3(0.7)	205.8(1.6)	219.5(3.5)	243.5(2.1)	268.4(1.5)	290.5(2.3)	311.0(1.9)	321.5(2.1)
LOW ABILITY	244.0(3.7)	39.3(1.7)	178.2(4.3)	193.6(4.8)	216.9(4.3)	245.1(4.0)	271.9(2.5)	293.3(3.0)	308.7(4.5)
MIXED ABILITY	263.3(2.8)	39.3(1.3)	196.4(6.2)	210.3(4.7)	237.1(2.4)	265.0(2.3)	291.3(3.9)	313.1(3.5)	324.9(5.4)

The standard errors of the estimated proficiencies appear in parentheses. It can be said with 95 percent certainty that for each population of interest the value for the whole population is within plus or minus two standard errors of the estimate for the sample.

!Interpret with caution -- the nature of the sample does not allow accurate determination of the variability of this estimated statistic.

	MEAN	STD DEV	5TH	10TH	25TH	50TH	75TH	90TH	95TH
-- TOTAL	293.5(1.2)	42.5(0.6)	221.7(1.8)	237.5(1.9)	265.0(1.6)	294.1(1.2)	323.2(1.1)	348.5(1.7)	362.4(1.7)
SEX									
MALE	298.9(1.5)	43.9(0.7)	224.2(3.7)	240.6(2.1)	268.8(2.6)	299.3(1.6)	330.4(1.8)	356.4(1.7)	369.5(1.6)
FEMALE	288.6(1.2)	40.6(0.8)	219.7(2.4)	235.1(1.9)	261.7(1.8)	290.0(1.7)	316.8(1.8)	339.7(1.5)	353.1(2.8)
RACE/ETHNICITY									
WHITE	302.5(1.3)	38.8(0.6)	237.7(2.4)	251.5(1.9)	276.6(1.5)	302.6(1.5)	329.4(1.2)	353.1(2.6)	365.8(2.2)
BLACK	256.3(2.4)	38.5(1.7)	194.8(3.6)	208.1(3.0)	229.4(2.1)	256.5(1.9)	281.8(2.6)	304.3(2.8)	319.6(4.1)
HISPANIC	272.5(2.8)	38.7(1.6)	211.0(5.7)	223.1(6.3)	245.5(3.2)	272.3(4.2)	297.4(3.8)	322.9(3.8)	337.7(7.5)
ASIAN/	308.2(7.1)	42.5(2.1)	230.2(21.6)	249.6(8.4)	280.3(14.7)	311.0(10.0)	338.8(9.9)	360.9(10.3)	372.2(11.9)
AMERICAN INDIAN/ ALASKAN NATIVE!	285.7(4.6)	31.6(4.2)	236.8(7.2)	246.6(12.3)	262.8(10.5)	284.7(24.9)	308.0(11.1)	329.7(9.7)	344.5(14.9)
REGION									
NORTHEAST	300.3(3.3)	42.1(1.2)	226.7(6.0)	243.5(4.6)	272.9(4.5)	301.8(2.3)	330.2(2.3)	354.3(4.8)	366.3(4.9)
SOUTHEAST	278.7(2.7)	40.6(1.0)	212.9(2.4)	225.3(3.2)	249.9(4.4)	278.8(3.7)	307.9(2.6)	331.1(2.3)	344.1(3.7)
CENTRAL	295.4(2.0)	41.7(1.6)	223.2(5.2)	241.5(2.7)	268.5(2.3)	296.4(2.6)	324.1(2.5)	348.5(2.7)	362.7(5.4)
WEST	296.7(2.9)	42.5(1.4)	226.4(4.0)	241.4(3.0)	268.1(3.3)	295.8(2.8)	326.4(4.4)	353.4(4.8)	366.5(3.7)
TYPE OF COMMUNITY									
EXTREME RURAL!	290.7(3.9)	39.4(1.9)	224.6(6.9)	240.8(5.8)	263.6(5.7)	289.8(3.9)	319.0(3.8)	341.7(4.9)	354.4(5.5)
DISADVANTAGED URBAN	272.9(5.3)	43.4(2.3)	204.0(13.7)	218.0(5.5)	242.2(6.1)	273.4(9.6)	302.7(5.6)	329.8(2.8)	345.6(5.2)
ADVANTAGED URBAN!	304.1(4.4)	44.1(2.3)	223.2(6.8)	243.3(5.4)	278.6(6.1)	305.9(4.3)	336.0(6.8)	357.2(8.0)	372.9(4.3)
OTHER	296.2(1.6)	41.4(0.7)	226.8(2.7)	241.8(2.2)	268.4(2.4)	296.5(1.6)	324.8(2.2)	350.2(2.5)	363.6(1.8)
PARENTS' EDUCATION LEVEL									
LESS THAN H.S.	269.0(2.5)	37.8(1.6)	209.1(5.7)	222.5(3.0)	242.8(3.4)	266.9(3.9)	294.8(9.4)	319.1(4.3)	334.2(4.7)
GRADUATED H.S.	278.9(1.3)	38.6(0.8)	214.5(2.8)	228.9(2.4)	252.7(2.9)	280.0(1.9)	305.7(1.3)	328.2(1.9)	341.5(3.5)
SOME EDUCATION AFTER H.S.	295.2(1.3)	38.3(0.9)	229.4(3.4)	245.6(3.5)	270.4(1.8)	295.5(1.3)	321.6(1.5)	344.6(2.3)	357.7(5.1)
GRADUATED COLLEGE	308.2(1.4)	41.3(0.8)	236.3(2.5)	252.9(1.8)	281.2(1.0)	309.8(1.5)	337.8(2.2)	360.5(3.1)	372.3(1.5)
UNKNOWN	249.0(5.3)	44.0(4.7)	177.9(8.2)	194.1(12.4)	216.8(7.8)	248.7(7.0)	279.2(12.0)	301.7(4.5)	314.7(7.8)
TYPE OF SCHOOL									
PUBLIC	292.7(1.3)	42.9(0.7)	220.2(2.0)	236.2(1.5)	263.6(1.5)	293.2(1.7)	322.7(1.6)	348.5(1.9)	362.4(1.5)
PRIVATE	301.2(2.8)	37.8(1.3)	237.3(3.1)	251.6(2.8)	275.8(3.4)	302.2(2.7)	326.8(2.3)	349.6(2.8)	361.4(6.6)
TYPE OF HIGH SCHOOL PROGRAM									
GENERAL	276.8(1.4)	37.5(0.8)	214.3(1.9)	228.9(2.4)	251.6(2.1)	277.3(2.0)	301.0(1.5)	324.4(2.4)	340.0(4.5)
ACADEMIC/COLLEGE PREP	308.7(1.3)	39.5(0.8)	240.5(2.0)	256.9(1.5)	283.3(1.2)	310.5(1.3)	336.2(1.5)	358.4(3.0)	370.0(2.0)
VOCATIONAL/TECHNICAL	264.8(2.4)	37.1(1.4)	203.2(2.5)	215.4(2.1)	328.6(3.7)	266.3(3.3)	291.8(2.5)	311.4(2.5)	323.1(5.4)

The standard errors of the estimated proficiencies appear in parentheses. It can be said with 95 percent certainty that for each population of interest the value for the whole population is within plus or minus two standard errors of the estimate for the sample.

!Interpret with caution -- the nature of the sample does not allow accurate determination of the variability of this estimated statistic.

	N	WEIGHTED PCT [CV]	200	250	300	350
-- TOTAL --	6314	100.0(0.0) [1%]	84.5(0.8)	30.6(1.3)	1.0(0.2)	0.0(0.0)
SEX						
MALE	3220	51.2(0.7) [2%]	84.6(1.0)	32.3(1.7)	1.1(0.2)	0.0(0.0)
FEMALE	3094	48.8(0.7) [2%]	84.4(1.0)	28.7(1.6)	0.8(0.3)	0.0(0.0)
RACE/ETHNICITY						
WHITE	3715	70.2(0.5) [1%]	93.1(0.8)	39.6(1.6)	1.3(0.3)	0.0(0.0)
BLACK	1075	15.2(0.4) [2%]	58.1(2.7)	5.2(1.1)	0.1(0.2)	0.0(0.0)
HISPANIC	1161	11.0(0.3) [3%]	65.9(2.4)	9.8(1.2)	0.0(0.0)	0.0(0.0)
ASIAN/PACIFIC ISLANDER	199	1.9(0.3) [16%]	87.5(3.1)	29.2(5.2)	1.8(1.5)	0.0(0.0)
AMERICAN INDIAN/ ALASKAN NATIVE	157	1.6(0.3) [18%]	81.3(5.3)	20.2(4.8)	0.0(0.0)	0.0(0.0)
REGION						
NORTHEAST	1278	21.5(0.8) [4%]	85.6(1.8)	35.5(3.0)	1.4(0.7)	0.0(0.0)
SOUTHEAST	1634	24.3(0.8) [3%]	80.2(2.5)	23.3(2.5)	0.6(0.2)	0.0(0.0)
CENTRAL	1505	26.5(0.8) [3%]	87.0(2.0)	30.9(3.1)	0.6(0.3)	0.0(0.0)
WEST	1897	27.6(0.8) [3%]	85.1(1.7)	32.8(2.8)	1.3(0.3)	0.0(0.0)
TYPE OF COMMUNITY						
EXTREME RURAL	491	10.8(1.8) [16%]	89.4(2.7)	29.9(3.5)	0.4(0.4)	0.0(0.0)
DISADVANTAGED URBAN	767	9.4(1.1) [12%]	59.4(3.9)	9.6(2.0)	0.1(0.0)	0.0(0.0)
ADVANTAGED URBAN	753	11.1(1.7) [15%]	96.2(1.5)	54.7(3.9)	2.5(0.9)	0.0(0.0)
OTHER	4303	68.6(2.8) [4%]	85.3(1.1)	29.6(1.4)	0.9(0.2)	0.0(0.0)
PARENTS' EDUCATION LEVEL						
LESS THAN H.S.	307	5.1(0.4) [8%]	78.0(3.7)	16.4(4.2)	0.0(0.0)	0.0(0.0)
GRADUATED H.S.	928	15.7(0.7) [4%]	80.9(1.8)	20.9(2.0)	0.4(0.3)	0.0(0.0)
SOME EDUCATION AFTER H.S.	524	8.6(0.4) [5%]	91.0(1.4)	42.4(2.9)	1.0(0.8)	0.0(0.0)
GRADUATED COLLEGE	2290	35.2(1.1) [3%]	89.9(0.9)	44.2(1.9)	2.0(0.3)	0.0(0.0)
UNKNOWN	2224	34.8(0.8) [2%]	80.5(1.1)	20.7(1.3)	0.3(0.3)	0.0(0.0)
TYPE OF SCHOOL						
PUBLIC	5092	88.8(1.1) [2%]	83.4(1.0)	29.1(1.4)	0.9(0.2)	0.0(0.0)
PRIVATE	1222	11.2(1.1) [10%]	93.5(1.2)	42.1(3.1)	1.5(0.4)	0.0(0.0)

The standard errors of the estimated proficiencies appear in parentheses. It can be said with 95 percent certainty that for each population of interest, the value for the whole population is within plus or minus two standard errors of the estimate for the sample.

	N	WEIGHTED PCT [CV]	200	250	300	350
-- TOTAL --	6531	100.0(0.0) [1%]	93.6(0.6)	64.1(1.2)	17.9(1.0)	0.7(0.2)
SEX						
MALE	3228	50.1(0.8) [2%]	93.5(0.8)	64.7(1.6)	21.1(1.5)	1.0(0.4)
FEMALE	3303	49.9(0.8) [2%]	93.7(0.8)	63.4(1.5)	14.7(1.2)	0.3(0.1)
RACE/ETHNICITY						
WHITE	4223	70.8(0.4) [1%]	97.4(0.5)	74.1(1.3)	23.1(1.3)	0.9(0.3)
BLACK	917	14.8(0.4) [3%]	79.9(2.5)	31.3(2.5)	2.5(0.8)	0.1(0.1)
HISPANIC	1000	10.1(0.3) [3%]	86.6(1.7)	41.7(2.8)	4.8(0.9)	0.1(0.1)
ASIAN/PACIFIC ISLANDER	285	2.7(0.4) [14%]	96.4(1.9)	71.4(4.8)	22.5(4.1)	0.7(0.6)
AMERICAN INDIAN/ ALASKAN NATIVE!	95	1.4(0.5) [36%]	91.8(2.8)	53.6(11.6)	7.8(2.8)	0.0(0.0)
REGION						
NORTHEAST	1506	21.0(1.0) [5%]	94.7(1.5)	70.7(2.9)	22.0(2.0)	0.8(0.4)
SOUTHEAST	1600	24.3(0.8) [3%]	91.9(1.5)	57.5(2.0)	13.1(1.3)	0.6(0.3)
CENTRAL	1383	24.8(0.7) [3%]	93.7(1.2)	66.8(2.6)	18.3(1.4)	0.4(0.4)
WEST	2042	30.0(0.9) [3%]	94.0(1.2)	62.6(2.5)	18.6(2.9)	0.9(0.4)
TYPE OF COMMUNITY						
EXTREME RURAL	641	11.4(2.1) [18%]	93.4(1.7)	58.3(4.1)	13.3(2.4)	0.4(0.3)
DISADVANTAGED URBAN	810	9.2(1.7) [19%]	83.5(3.2)	43.0(3.8)	8.0(1.7)	0.3(0.2)
ADVANTAGED URBAN!	808	10.4(2.2) [22%]	98.7(0.6)	82.4(2.6)	33.5(5.4)	1.9(1.0)
OTHER	4272	69.1(2.8) [4%]	94.2(0.8)	65.1(1.5)	17.6(1.1)	0.6(0.3)
PARENTS' EDUCATION LEVEL						
LESS THAN H.S.	584	8.8(0.6) [7%]	88.6(2.9)	41.0(3.0)	3.6(1.2)	0.1(0.0)
GRADUATED H.S.	1540	24.8(0.8) [3%]	92.0(1.0)	56.2(1.8)	9.9(0.9)	0.1(0.2)
SOME EDUCATION AFTER H.S.	1195	18.7(0.8) [4%]	95.9(0.7)	71.6(1.9)	18.6(1.7)	0.6(0.4)
GRADUATED COLLEGE	2642	39.6(1.6) [4%]	96.9(0.5)	76.2(1.5)	28.5(2.0)	1.3(0.3)
UNKNOWN	559	7.9(0.4) [5%]	82.4(2.4)	36.4(2.4)	4.5(1.0)	0.0(0.0)
TYPE OF SCHOOL						
PUBLIC	5206	88.6(1.3) [2%]	93.0(0.7)	62.5(1.3)	17.2(1.1)	0.6(0.2)
PRIVATE	1325	11.4(1.3) [12%]	98.2(0.8)	76.3(2.3)	23.2(1.7)	1.2(0.5)
ABILITY OF STUDENTS IN CLASS						
HIGH ABILITY	817	11.4(1.0) [9%]	99.3(0.8)	87.8(2.1)	39.9(2.9)	2.0(1.1)
AVERAGE ABILITY	1685	25.8(1.7) [6%]	96.2(0.6)	68.8(1.7)	17.5(1.4)	0.5(0.3)
LOW ABILITY	533	7.8(1.3) [16%]	86.7(2.7)	45.0(4.2)	7.7(1.4)	0.1(0.0)
MIXED ABILITY	1590	26.4(2.3) [9%]	93.9(1.5)	63.9(2.6)	17.9(2.6)	0.8(0.4)

The standard errors of the estimated proficiencies appear in parentheses. It can be said with 95 percent certainty that for each population of interest, the value for the whole population is within plus or minus two standard errors of the estimate for the sample.

! Interpret with caution -- the nature of the sample does not allow accurate determination of the variability of this estimated statistic.

NAEP 1990 SCIENCE CROSS-SECTIONAL ASSESSMENT—GRADE 12
Percentage of Students with Science Proficiency
At or Above Four Anchor Levels

	N	WEIGHTED PCT [CV]	200	250	300	350
-- TOTAL --	6337	100.0(0.0) [1%]	98.6(0.2)	84.1(0.9)	44.7(1.2)	9.4(0.8)
SEX						
MALE	3058	48.2(0.8) [2%]	98.9(0.3)	85.9(1.0)	49.4(1.4)	13.2(1.1)
FEMALE	3279	51.8(0.8) [2%]	98.2(0.3)	82.5(1.1)	40.3(1.3)	5.9(0.7)
RACE/ETHNICITY						
WHITE	4443	73.2(0.4) [1%]	99.6(0.1)	90.7(0.8)	52.8(1.4)	11.5(0.9)
BLACK	872	14.2(0.5) [3%]	93.5(1.4)	56.8(3.0)	12.0(2.0)	1.1(0.6)
HISPANIC	700	8.2(0.3) [4%]	97.5(0.8)	70.3(3.4)	23.1(2.9)	2.9(1.0)
ASIAN/PACIFIC ISLANDER	263	3.6(0.2) [5%]	99.1(1.4)	89.7(3.2)	59.9(7.4)	16.7(5.0)
AMERICAN INDIAN/ ALASKAN NATIVE!	51	0.7(0.2) [36%]	99.6(0.7)	88.9(5.6)	33.1(9.3)	2.2(0.0)
REGION						
NORTHEAST	1628	23.8(1.0) [4%]	98.9(0.5)	87.4(2.4)	52.0(2.9)	12.0(2.0)
SOUTHEAST	1728	20.6(0.8) [4%]	97.8(0.6)	75.1(2.4)	31.2(2.5)	3.5(0.8)
CENTRAL	1277	26.5(0.5) [2%]	98.5(0.5)	86.2(1.4)	46.6(2.0)	9.3(1.5)
WEST	1704	29.1(0.9) [3%]	98.9(0.4)	86.0(1.8)	46.4(2.6)	11.5(1.7)
TYPE OF COMMUNITY						
EXTREME RURAL!	647	10.9(2.7) [25%]	99.1(0.6)	84.8(3.0)	41.0(3.8)	6.6(1.7)
DISADVANTAGED URBAN	821	12.3(2.5) [20%]	95.8(1.8)	68.9(5.0)	27.4(3.7)	4.0(1.0)
ADVANTAGED URBAN!	786	10.2(2.4) [24%]	98.6(0.9)	87.4(2.8)	56.5(4.4)	14.2(2.2)
OTHER	4083	66.6(3.5) [5%]	99.0(0.2)	86.3(1.1)	46.6(1.5)	10.1(1.1)
PARENTS' EDUCATION LEVEL						
LESS THAN H.S.	490	7.5(0.6) [8%]	97.5(0.7)	67.6(3.3)	21.0(2.8)	1.7(1.0)
GRADUATED H.S.	1443	23.7(0.8) [3%]	97.9(0.6)	77.1(1.6)	29.9(1.4)	3.2(0.7)
SOME EDUCATION AFTER H.S.	1602	26.0(0.8) [3%]	99.3(0.2)	87.8(1.3)	45.1(1.7)	7.6(1.0)
GRADUATED COLLEGE	2656	40.4(1.3) [3%]	99.4(0.2)	91.2(0.7)	59.4(1.6)	16.1(1.5)
UNKNOWN	130	2.1(0.2) [11%]	86.6(3.9)	47.6(7.5)	11.8(2.7)	2.2(2.2)
TYPE OF SCHOOL						
PUBLIC	4956	90.2(1.4) [2%]	98.5(0.2)	83.4(0.9)	43.8(1.3)	9.3(0.8)
PRIVATE	1381	9.8(1.4) [14%]	99.6(0.2)	90.7(1.5)	52.1(2.7)	9.8(1.7)
TYPE OF HIGH SCHOOL PROGRAM						
GENERAL	2035	34.3(1.1) [3%]	98.0(0.4)	76.3(1.6)	26.2(1.6)	2.9(0.7)
ACADEMIC/COLLEGE PREP	3773	56.5(1.3) [2%]	99.4(0.2)	92.5(0.7)	60.4(1.4)	14.7(1.1)
VOCATIONAL/TECHNICAL	469	8.3(0.6) [7%]	96.0(1.1)	64.5(3.4)	17.8(2.3)	0.9(0.6)

The standard errors of the estimated proficiencies appear in parentheses. It can be said with 95 percent certainty that for each population of interest, the value for the whole population is within plus or minus two standard errors of the estimate for the sample.

! Interpret with caution -- the nature of the sample does not allow accurate determination of the variability of this estimated statistic.

Percentages of Students and Mean Proficiencies for the Nation and Demographic Subpopulations by Gender

	MALE	FEMALE
-- TOTAL --	51.2(0.7)	48.8(0.7)
	233.8(1.1)	231.7(1.0)
SEX		
MALE	100.0(0.0)	0.0(0.0)
	233.8(1.1)	*****(0.0)
FEMALE	0.0(0.0)	100.0(0.0)
	*****(0.0)	231.7(1.0)
RACE/ETHNICITY		
WHITE	51.5(1.0)	48.5(1.0)
	243.2(1.3)	240.9(1.1)
BLACK	48.7(1.6)	51.3(1.6)
	204.9(1.8)	205.8(1.8)
HISPANIC	51.9(1.6)	48.1(1.6)
	213.0(1.6)	211.0(1.9)
ASIAN/PACIFIC ISLANDER	51.0(4.0)	49.0(4.0)
	231.6(3.2)	234.9(4.4)
AMERICAN INDIAN/ ALASKAN NATIVE	57.5(4.2)	42.5(4.2)
	227.1(3.4)	224.8(4.0)
REGION		
NORTHEAST	51.3(1.4)	48.7(1.4)
	237.9(2.3)	233.2(1.7)
SOUTHEAST	51.1(1.7)	48.9(1.7)
	228.0(2.7)	225.3(2.1)
CENTRAL	52.7(1.9)	47.3(1.9)
	235.3(2.5)	233.2(2.4)
WEST	49.7(1.0)	50.3(1.0)
	234.2(1.7)	234.6(2.7)
TYPE OF COMMUNITY		
EXTREME RURAL	54.4(2.5)	45.6(2.5)
	236.3(3.6)	233.5(2.2)
DISADVANTAGED URBAN	53.1(2.0)	46.9(2.0)
	210.3(3.1)	206.5(2.7)
ADVANTAGED URBAN	50.3(2.8)	49.7(2.8)
	251.7(2.9)	251.6(2.5)
OTHER	50.5(1.0)	49.5(1.0)
	233.9(1.2)	231.4(1.1)
PARENTS' EDUCATION LEVEL		
LESS THAN H.S.	50.3(3.4)	49.7(3.4)
	222.2(3.4)	220.6(2.8)
GRADUATED H.S.	51.3(1.7)	48.7(1.7)
	228.2(1.8)	223.1(1.9)
SOME EDUCATION AFTER H.S.	50.8(2.7)	49.2(2.7)
	243.7(2.5)	240.1(2.6)
GRADUATED COLLEGE	54.0(1.3)	46.0(1.3)
	243.0(1.5)	242.2(1.4)
UNKNOWN	48.3(1.1)	51.7(1.1)
	225.8(1.2)	225.8(1.1)
TYPE OF SCHOOL		
PUBLIC	50.9(0.8)	49.1(0.8)
	232.4(1.1)	230.4(1.2)
PRIVATE	53.6(2.2)	46.4(2.2)
	244.4(2.7)	242.3(1.8)

The standard errors of the estimated proficiencies appear in parentheses. It can be said with 95 percent certainty that for each population of interest, the value for the whole population is within plus or minus two standard errors of the estimate for the sample.

	WHITE	BLACK	HISPANIC	ASIAN PACIFIC/ISLANDER	AMERICAN INDIAN/ ALASKAN NATIVE	OTHER
-- TOTAL --	70.2(0.5)	15.2(0.4)	11.0(0.3)	1.9(0.3)	1.6(0.3)	0.1(0.0)
	242.1(1.0)	205.4(1.5)	212.0(1.5)	233.2(3.0)	226.1(2.7)	223.0(24.3)
SEX						
MALE	70.7(0.7)	14.4(0.5)	11.1(0.5)	1.9(0.3)	1.8(0.3)	0.1(0.0)
	243.2(1.3)	204.9(1.8)	213.0(1.6)	231.6(3.2)	227.1(3.4)	250.3(3.8)
FEMALE	69.7(0.7)	16.0(0.7)	10.8(0.5)	1.9(0.3)	1.4(0.3)	0.2(0.1)
	240.9(1.1)	205.8(1.8)	211.0(1.9)	234.9(4.4)	224.8(4.0)	212.7(32.7)
RACE/ETHNICITY						
WHITE	100.0(0.0)	0.0(0.0)	0.0(0.0)	0.0(0.0)	0.0(0.0)	0.0(0.0)
	242.1(1.0)	*****(0.0)	*****(0.0)	*****(0.0)	*****(0.0)	*****(0.0)
BLACK	0.0(0.0)	100.0(0.0)	0.0(0.0)	0.0(0.0)	0.0(0.0)	0.0(0.0)
	*****(0.0)	205.4(1.5)	*****(0.0)	*****(0.0)	*****(0.0)	*****(0.0)
HISPANIC	0.0(0.0)	0.0(0.0)	100.0(0.0)	0.0(0.0)	0.0(0.0)	0.0(0.0)
	*****(0.0)	*****(0.0)	212.0(1.5)	*****(0.0)	*****(0.0)	*****(0.0)
ASIAN/PACIFIC ISLANDER	0.0(0.0)	0.0(0.0)	0.0(0.0)	100.0(0.0)	0.0(0.0)	0.0(0.0)
	*****(0.0)	*****(0.0)	*****(0.0)	233.2(3.0)	*****(0.0)	*****(0.0)
AMERICAN INDIAN/ ALASKAN NATIVE	0.0(0.0)	0.0(0.0)	0.0(0.0)	0.0(0.0)	100.0(0.0)	0.0(0.0)
	*****(0.0)	*****(0.0)	*****(0.0)	*****(0.0)	226.1(2.7)	*****(0.0)
REGION						
NORTHEAST	73.2(2.0)	15.3(1.9)	9.7(1.0)	0.7(0.2)	1.1(0.3)	0.0(0.0)
	246.7(2.1)	199.7(3.1)	209.9(3.3)	228.3(5.3)	229.2(5.8)	*****(0.0)
SOUTHEAST	63.6(1.9)	26.5(1.7)	8.1(0.9)	0.5(0.2)	1.2(0.3)	0.1(0.1)
	236.7(2.7)	208.4(2.0)	208.7(3.3)	226.7(8.0)	225.7(5.0)	187.3(****)
CENTRAL	78.4(2.0)	12.3(1.7)	6.4(0.6)	0.8(0.2)	2.0(0.4)	0.2(0.0)
	240.9(1.6)	202.3(4.2)	217.2(3.7)	244.3(11.6)	221.6(4.1)	232.7(12.7)
WEST	65.8(1.9)	7.9(1.3)	19.0(1.1)	5.1(1.2)	2.1(0.6)	0.1(0.1)
	244.0(1.8)	209.4(3.1)	212.5(2.3)	232.8(3.4)	229.1(5.3)	252.7(7.7)
TYPE OF COMMUNITY						
EXTREME RURAL	85.6(2.1)	5.3(1.7)	6.4(0.9)	0.3(0.2)	2.1(0.8)	0.3(0.3)
	237.8(2.6)	208.7(5.1)	223.6(4.5)	243.5(47.2)	229.9(7.2)	187.3(****)
DISADVANTAGED URBAN	35.3(4.3)	36.9(4.6)	23.1(2.7)	2.6(0.9)	1.9(0.5)	0.2(0.2)
	231.0(2.9)	193.7(2.3)	197.3(3.5)	213.3(3.4)	207.8(4.1)	243.1(****)
ADVANTAGED URBAN	80.4(2.7)	6.3(1.6)	7.7(0.9)	4.4(1.7)	1.1(0.3)	0.1(0.1)
	255.7(2.2)	221.5(8.3)	233.3(4.4)	254.4(10.3)	243.6(7.8)	261.5(10.3)
OTHER	70.9(1.0)	15.2(0.9)	10.6(0.5)	1.6(0.3)	1.6(0.3)	0.1(0.0)
	241.1(1.0)	208.0(2.0)	212.8(1.6)	228.0(3.8)	226.5(3.6)	234.6(18.4)
PARENTS' EDUCATION LEVEL						
LESS THAN H.S.	67.8(3.4)	12.5(2.3)	16.4(2.3)	1.5(0.7)	1.8(0.9)	0.0(0.0)
	228.4(2.7)	206.3(5.3)	204.8(3.3)	226.4(11.4)	209.8(7.2)	*****(0.0)
GRADUATED H.S.	69.8(1.7)	16.8(1.2)	10.8(0.9)	0.7(0.2)	1.7(0.5)	0.2(0.2)
	234.5(1.5)	201.9(2.6)	208.2(3.1)	219.9(7.0)	219.4(6.8)	187.3(****)
SOME EDUCATION AFTER H.S.	77.0(1.6)	10.9(1.4)	9.3(1.1)	1.5(0.5)	1.3(0.4)	0.0(0.0)
	249.6(1.8)	206.8(4.5)	220.7(4.1)	243.3(8.1)	231.2(7.5)	*****(0.0)
GRADUATED COLLEGE	71.2(1.1)	16.6(0.8)	8.6(0.5)	2.0(0.4)	1.4(0.3)	0.1(0.1)
	252.7(1.2)	210.7(2.3)	221.8(2.2)	246.0(5.1)	234.4(5.2)	246.4(6.3)
UNKNOWN	68.0(0.8)	14.3(0.8)	13.2(0.6)	2.5(0.4)	1.9(0.4)	0.1(0.1)
	234.7(1.0)	201.1(2.0)	207.0(2.1)	224.2(3.2)	223.9(4.0)	233.6(12.6)
TYPE OF SCHOOL						
PUBLIC	69.0(0.6)	16.0(0.5)	11.4(0.3)	1.7(0.2)	1.7(0.3)	0.1(0.0)
	241.3(1.1)	204.4(1.5)	210.9(1.6)	230.4(3.6)	225.2(2.8)	220.4(25.3)
PRIVATE	79.6(2.3)	8.3(1.4)	8.1(1.3)	3.0(1.2)	0.9(0.3)	0.1(0.1)
	247.6(1.9)	221.1(4.1)	224.3(4.8)	246.1(7.1)	241.1(4.4)	268.2(****)

152   The standard errors of the estimated proficiencies appear in parentheses. It can be said with 95 percent certainty that for each population of interest, the value for the whole population is within plus or minus two standard errors of the estimate for the sample.

NAEP 1990 SCIENCE CROSS-SECTIONAL ASSESSMENT—GRADE 8
Percentages of Students and Mean Proficiencies for the Nation and Demographic Subpopulations by Gender

	MALE	FEMALE
-- TOTAL --	50.1(0.8)	49.9(0.8)
	265.1(1.6)	261.0(1.2)
SEX		
MALE	100.0(0.0)	0.0(0.0)
	265.1(1.6)	*****(0.0)
FEMALE	0.0(0.0)	100.0(0.0)
	*****(0.0)	261.0(1.2)
RACE/ETHNICITY		
WHITE	50.9(1.0)	49.1(1.0)
	274.4(1.8)	271.3(1.4)
BLACK	45.1(1.7)	54.9(1.7)
	231.9(2.9)	230.3(2.1)
HISPANIC	51.9(1.6)	48.1(1.6)
	243.1(3.0)	239.1(2.5)
ASIAN/PACIFIC ISLANDER	52.9(3.8)	47.1(3.8)
	272.5(4.7)	268.3(4.5)
AMERICAN INDIAN/ ALASKAN NATIVE!	42.0(5.4)	58.0(5.4)
	255.2(10.3)	249.5(7.8)
REGION		
NORTHEAST	51.5(1.8)	48.5(1.8)
	270.7(3.6)	267.6(3.1)
SOUTHEAST	47.5(1.4)	52.5(1.4)
	259.5(2.2)	253.3(2.3)
CENTRAL	50.9(2.0)	49.1(2.0)
	266.1(2.8)	262.8(2.6)
WEST	50.5(1.0)	49.5(1.0)
	264.7(3.7)	261.5(2.4)
TYPE OF COMMUNITY		
EXTREME RURAL	50.8(2.3)	49.2(2.3)
	258.8(3.4)	256.0(5.0)
DISADVANTAGED URBAN	52.2(1.8)	47.8(1.8)
	242.5(4.3)	241.8(4.7)
ADVANTAGED URBAN!	49.2(1.5)	50.8(1.5)
	286.4(5.0)	280.5(4.0)
OTHER	49.8(1.0)	50.2(1.0)
	266.2(1.8)	261.2(1.5)
PARENTS' EDUCATION LEVEL		
LESS THAN H.S.	40.4(2.3)	59.6(2.3)
	244.8(3.3)	238.7(2.8)
GRADUATED H.S.	50.1(1.4)	49.9(1.4)
	255.9(1.8)	252.3(1.5)
SOME EDUCATION AFTER H.S.	46.0(1.4)	54.0(1.4)
	270.3(2.3)	266.7(1.5)
GRADUATED COLLEGE	52.6(1.2)	47.4(1.2)
	277.4(2.0)	275.3(1.9)
UNKNOWN	57.2(2.7)	42.8(2.7)
	240.6(3.0)	231.0(2.7)
TYPE OF SCHOOL		
PUBLIC	50.1(0.8)	49.9(0.8)
	263.5(1.7)	259.6(1.4)
PRIVATE	50.1(1.6)	49.9(1.6)
	277.6(2.4)	272.1(2.7)
ABILITY OF STUDENTS IN CLASS		
HIGH ABILITY	48.0(1.9)	52.0(1.9)
	294.3(2.6)	285.3(2.1)
AVERAGE ABILITY	49.5(1.4)	50.5(1.4)
	268.4(2.0)	264.6(1.5)
LOW ABILITY	49.9(2.6)	50.1(2.6)
	246.5(4.9)	241.5(4.0)
MIXED ABILITY	50.6(1.4)	49.4(1.4)
	267.3(2.9)	259.3(3.1)

The standard errors of the estimated proficiencies appear in parentheses. It can be said with 95 percent certainty that for each population of interest, the value for the whole population is within plus or minus two standard errors of the estimate for the sample.

!Interpret with caution -- the nature of the sample does not allow accurate determination of the variability of this estimated statistic.

	WHITE	BLACK	HISPANIC	ASIAN PACIFIC/ISLANDER	AMERICAN INDIAN/ ALASKAN NATIVE	OTHER
-- TOTAL --	70.8(0.4) 272.9(1.4)	14.8(0.4) 231.0(2.2)	10.1(0.3) 241.2(2.1)	2.7(0.4) 270.5(4.0)	1.4(0.5) 251.9(8.5)	0.1(0.0) 255.1(12.8)
SEX						
MALE	72.0(0.7) 274.4(1.8)	13.4(0.6) 231.9(2.9)	10.5(0.4) 243.1(3.0)	2.9(0.4) 272.5(4.7)	1.2(0.4) 255.2(10.3)	0.1(0.1) 273.9(12.8)
FEMALE	69.6(0.7) 271.3(1.4)	16.3(0.6) 230.3(2.1)	9.8(0.4) 239.1(2.5)	2.6(0.5) 268.3(4.5)	1.6(0.6) 249.5(7.8)	0.1(0.1) 234.8(14.5)
RACE/ETHNICITY						
WHITE	100.0(0.0) 272.9(1.4)	0.0(0.0) *****(0.0)	0.0(0.0) *****(0.0)	0.0(0.0) *****(0.0)	0.0(0.0) *****(0.0)	0.0(0.0) *****(0.0)
BLACK	0.0(0.0) *****(0.0)	100.0(0.0) 231.0(2.2)	0.0(0.0) *****(0.0)	0.0(0.0) *****(0.0)	0.0(0.0) *****(0.0)	0.0(0.0) *****(0.0)
HISPANIC	0.0(0.0) *****(0.0)	0.0(0.0) *****(0.0)	100.0(0.0) 241.2(2.1)	0.0(0.0) *****(0.0)	0.0(0.0) *****(0.0)	0.0(0.0) *****(0.0)
ASIAN/PACIFIC ISLANDER	0.0(0.0) *****(0.0)	0.0(0.0) *****(0.0)	0.0(0.0) *****(0.0)	100.0(0.0) 270.5(4.0)	0.0(0.0) *****(0.0)	0.0(0.0) *****(0.0)
AMERICAN INDIAN/ ALASKAN NATIVE!	0.0(0.0) *****(0.0)	0.0(0.0) *****(0.0)	0.0(0.0) *****(0.0)	0.0(0.0) *****(0.0)	100.0(0.0) 251.9(8.5)	0.0(0.0) *****(0.0)
REGION						
NORTHEAST	76.4(3.4) 277.3(2.7)	12.3(2.7) 232.0(7.4)	7.0(0.9) 242.1(6.3)	3.5(1.0) 280.8(7.8)	0.7(0.4) 249.8(19.5)	0.1(0.1) 226.2(****)
SOUTHEAST	69.1(2.3) 267.2(1.7)	25.9(2.3) 228.8(3.3)	3.9(0.9) 242.0(4.5)	0.6(0.2) 272.3(6.2)	0.5(0.2) 258.3(12.5)	305.6(6.4)
CENTRAL	78.6(1.6) 272.0(2.2)	12.8(1.6) 230.3(5.6)	5.6(0.9) 240.2(4.9)	1.8(0.4) 268.3(8.3)	1.0(0.3) 248.0(11.2)	0.2(0.1) 240.9(11.9)
WEST	61.8(1.7) 275.0(3.8)	9.3(2.0) 236.0(3.6)	21.2(1.2) 241.1(2.6)	4.6(1.5) 265.5(4.7)	2.9(1.6) 252.5(18.0)	0.1(0.1) 274.4(16.5)
TYPE OF COMMUNITY						
EXTREME RURAL	78.1(5.3) 263.7(3.6)	10.2(3.7) 227.2(7.4)	5.7(1.9) 237.1(9.2)	0.4(0.3) 237.5(30.3)	5.4(4.9) 246.4(19.4)	0.2(0.2) 273.8(34.3)
DISADVANTAGED URBAN	38.8(6.7) 263.2(4.7)	32.1(6.2) 221.2(4.8)	22.9(3.7) 233.6(4.7)	5.0(1.9) 257.5(7.0)	1.1(0.4) 222.4(13.4)	0.1(0.1) 226.2(****)
ADVANTAGED URBAN!	82.3(3.4) 287.0(3.8)	6.7(2.8) 245.6(7.8)	6.4(0.9) 270.2(5.2)	4.1(1.3) 294.5(7.7)	0.4(0.2) 280.4(5.7)	0.0(0.0) *****(0.0)
OTHER	72.1(1.5) 272.7(1.3)	14.5(1.0) 233.3(3.1)	9.7(0.8) 241.1(3.0)	2.6(0.6) 268.8(4.0)	0.9(0.2) 260.2(6.2)	0.1(0.0) 253.3(12.9)
PARENTS' EDUCATION LEVEL						
LESS THAN H.S.	60.7(2.7) 247.9(2.5)	15.4(1.8) 219.9(5.3)	21.2(1.9) 236.6(3.4)	1.3(0.5) 242.3(12.6)	1.3(0.6) 246.3(23.3)	0.1(0.1) 273.5(****)
GRADUATED H.S.	71.4(1.3) 263.2(1.5)	15.7(1.0) 223.6(2.7)	9.8(0.6) 238.1(2.7)	1.4(0.3) 261.0(9.2)	1.6(0.6) 239.8(13.7)	0.1(0.1) 218.8(10.2)
SOME EDUCATION AFTER H.S.	72.2(1.5) 276.3(1.7)	14.5(1.2) 240.8(3.7)	9.6(0.9) 248.6(2.8)	2.0(0.5) 275.1(5.8)	1.7(0.6) 269.9(16.5)	0.0(0.0) *****(0.0)
GRADUATED COLLEGE	76.5(1.0) 284.2(1.6)	13.1(0.8) 240.6(3.0)	5.6(0.5) 254.0(3.5)	3.7(0.5) 280.9(4.5)	1.0(0.4) 259.8(4.4)	0.2(0.1) 273.0(12.9)
UNKNOWN	48.8(1.9) 250.5(3.3)	21.0(2.0) 213.4(4.6)	22.8(1.9) 226.4(3.9)	5.3(1.4) 245.3(6.7)	1.9(0.7) 230.0(16.5)	0.1(0.2) 226.2(****)
TYPE OF SCHOOL						
PUBLIC	70.6(0.6) 271.9(1.5)	15.6(0.4) 229.6(2.3)	9.8(0.4) 238.3(2.1)	2.3(0.4) 266.7(5.1)	1.5(0.5) 250.9(8.4)	0.1(0.0) 252.4(14.4)
PRIVATE	72.1(3.4) 279.9(2.1)	8.8(2.1) 251.5(4.9)	12.5(1.7) 259.1(3.5)	5.9(1.9) 282.0(4.9)	0.5(0.2) 277.2(8.6)	0.2(0.1) 266.7(19.5)
ABILITY OF STUDENTS IN CLASS						
HIGH ABILITY	78.0(2.1) 295.2(1.9)	11.4(1.9) 258.7(3.9)	5.5(0.8) 271.6(5.1)	4.0(0.9) 295.4(6.9)	1.0(0.4) 289.2(15.7)	0.1(0.1) 242.9(19.9)
AVERAGE ABILITY	77.1(1.7) 273.2(1.6)	11.5(1.0) 237.5(3.6)	8.4(1.1) 246.0(3.0)	2.3(0.6) 261.5(4.9)	0.6(0.2) 272.6(5.6)	0.2(0.1) 228.5(18.8)
LOW ABILITY	62.1(3.6) 254.6(4.0)	23.8(3.4) 221.7(5.9)	10.8(2.1) 232.2(4.4)	1.9(0.7) 257.0(11.9)	1.3(0.6) 221.7(23.1)	0.1(0.1) 273.5(****)
MIXED ABILITY	72.9(2.5) 272.3(3.2)	15.7(2.1) 229.2(4.6)	8.5(1.2) 246.0(3.5)	1.8(0.5) 281.3(5.3)	0.9(0.3) 255.0(6.5)	0.2(0.1) 270.7(19.5)

The standard errors of the estimated proficiencies appear in parentheses. It can be said with 95 percent certainty that for each population of interest, the value for the whole population is within plus or minus two standard errors of the estimate for the sample.

!Interpret with caution -- the nature of the sample does not allow accurate determination of the variability of this estimated statistic.

NAEP 1990 SCIENCE CROSS-SECTIONAL ASSESSMENT— GRADE 12
Percentages of Students and Mean Proficiencies for the Nation and Demographic Subpopulations by Gender

	MALE	FEMALE
-- TOTAL --	48.2(0.8)	51.8(0.8)
	298.9(1.5)	288.6(1.2)
SEX		
MALE	100.0(0.0)	0.0(0.0)
	298.9(1.5)	*****(0.0)
FEMALE	0.0(0.0)	100.0(0.0)
	*****(0.0)	288.6(1.2)
RACE/ETHNICITY		
WHITE	49.0(1.0)	51.0(1.0)
	307.1(1.5)	298.0(1.3)
BLACK	43.3(2.2)	56.7(2.2)
	261.2(2.7)	252.6(2.9)
HISPANIC	49.1(2.9)	50.9(2.9)
	277.7(3.1)	267.5(3.5)
ASIAN/PACIFIC ISLANDER	46.0(2.3)	54.0(2.3)
	315.2(10.6)	302.3(5.0)
AMERICAN INDIAN/ ALASKAN NATIVE	56.9(7.7)	43.1(7.7)
	288.7(7.1)	281.8(5.9)
REGION		
NORTHEAST	47.8(1.5)	52.2(1.5)
	305.7(3.4)	295.4(3.4)
SOUTHEAST	46.4(1.7)	53.6(1.7)
	281.7(4.0)	276.2(2.2)
CENTRAL	50.6(1.9)	49.4(1.9)
	300.7(2.8)	289.9(2.4)
WEST	47.5(1.1)	52.5(1.1)
	303.4(3.2)	290.7(2.9)
TYPE OF COMMUNITY		
EXTREME RURAL!	48.6(2.5)	51.4(2.5)
	294.0(4.3)	287.6(4.2)
DISADVANTAGED URBAN	46.5(3.5)	53.5(3.5)
	280.8(4.1)	266.1(6.0)
ADVANTAGED URBAN!	47.2(2.2)	52.8(2.2)
	312.9(4.2)	296.1(5.3)
OTHER	48.6(1.0)	51.4(1.0)
	300.7(1.9)	291.8(1.5)
PARENTS' EDUCATION LEVEL		
LESS THAN H.S.	37.3(2.4)	62.7(2.4)
	276.5(4.3)	264.6(2.9)
GRADUATED H.S.	47.7(1.6)	52.3(1.6)
	283.3(2.0)	274.8(1.6)
SOME EDUCATION AFTER H.S.	48.7(1.6)	51.3(1.6)
	298.9(1.7)	291.7(1.7)
GRADUATED COLLEGE	49.9(1.0)	50.1(1.0)
	313.1(1.9)	303.3(1.3)
UNKNOWN	53.3(5.2)	46.7(5.2)
	260.5(6.8)	235.9(6.6)
TYPE OF SCHOOL		
PUBLIC	47.8(0.8)	52.2(0.8)
	298.4(1.7)	287.5(1.3)
PRIVATE	51.7(3.9)	48.3(3.9)
	303.0(4.2)	299.2(2.4)
TYPE OF HIGH SCHOOL PROGRAM		
GENERAL	50.1(1.0)	49.9(1.0)
	283.0(2.0)	270.7(1.7)
ACADEMIC/COLLEGE PREP	45.7(1.2)	54.3(1.2)
	315.8(1.7)	302.7(1.2)
VOCATIONAL/TECHNICAL	55.2(2.7)	44.8(2.7)
	270.1(3.4)	258.3(3.2)

The standard errors of the estimated proficiencies appear in parentheses. It can be said with 95 percent certainty that for each population of interest, the value for the whole population is within plus or minus two standard errors of the estimate for the sample.

!Interpret with caution -- the nature of the sample does not allow accurate determination of the variability of this estimated statistic.

	WHITE	BLACK	HISPANIC	ASIAN PACIFIC/ISLANDER	AMERICAN INDIAN/ ALASKAN NATIVE	OTHER
-- TOTAL --	73.2(0.4) 302.5(1.3)	14.2(0.5) 256.3(2.4)	8.2(0.3) 272.5(2.8)	3.6(0.2) 308.2(7.1)	0.7(0.2) 285.7(4.6)	0.1(0.0) 277.2(18.1)
SEX						
MALE	74.5(0.9) 307.1(1.5)	12.8(0.8) 261.2(2.7)	8.4(0.6) 277.7(3.1)	3.4(0.2) 315.2(10.6)	0.8(0.3) 288.7(7.1)	0.1(0.1) 271.7(35.7)
FEMALE	72.0(0.8) 298.0(1.3)	15.6(0.7) 252.6(2.9)	8.1(0.5) 267.5(3.5)	3.7(0.3) 302.3(5.0)	0.6(0.3) 281.8(5.9)	0.1(0.1) 284.4(9.6)
RACE/ETHNICITY						
WHITE	100.0(0.0) 302.5(1.3)	0.0(0.0) *****(0.0)	0.0(0.0) *****(0.0)	0.0(0.0) *****(0.0)	0.0(0.0) *****(0.0)	0.0(0.0) *****(0.0)
BLACK	0.0(0.0) *****(0.0)	100.0(0.0) 256.3(2.4)	0.0(0.0) *****(0.0)	0.0(0.0) *****(0.0)	0.0(0.0) *****(0.0)	0.0(0.0) *****(0.0)
HISPANIC	0.0(0.0) *****(0.0)	0.0(0.0) *****(0.0)	100.0(0.0) 272.5(2.8)	0.0(0.0) *****(0.0)	0.0(0.0) *****(0.0)	0.0(0.0) *****(0.0)
ASIAN/PACIFIC ISLANDER	0.0(0.0) *****(0.0)	0.0(0.0) *****(0.0)	0.0(0.0) *****(0.0)	100.0(0.0) 308.2(7.1)	0.0(0.0) *****(0.0)	0.0(0.0) *****(0.0)
AMERICAN INDIAN/ ALASKAN NATIVE!	0.0(0.0) *****(0.0)	0.0(0.0) *****(0.0)	0.0(0.0) *****(0.0)	0.0(0.0) *****(0.0)	100.0(0.0) 285.7(4.6)	0.0(0.0) *****(0.0)
REGION						
NORTHEAST	80.5(3.0) 306.9(2.2)	11.3(2.1) 261.6(6.1)	4.8(1.3) 269.6(8.0)	3.2(1.2) 318.5(9.1)	0.1(0.1) 280.4(13.4)	0.0(0.0) *****(0.0)
SOUTHEAST	64.3(2.4) 291.1(3.0)	29.3(2.2) 251.5(3.1)	4.4(1.0) 268.8(4.9)	1.4(0.6) 306.3(5.1)	0.6(0.3) 296.1(9.7)	0.0(0.0) *****(0.0)
CENTRAL	84.6(1.5) 301.4(2.5)	10.0(1.5) 251.4(7.0)	3.0(0.7) 268.5(5.9)	1.2(0.5) 319.3(14.8)	1.0(0.6) 284.8(7.0)	0.2(0.1) 282.9(21.2)
WEST	63.1(2.2) 307.5(2.7)	9.7(1.5) 266.3(5.0)	18.4(1.1) 274.3(3.7)	7.6(1.7) 303.4(10.3)	1.0(0.4) 282.8(9.2)	0.2(0.1) 272.9(33.0)
TYPE OF COMMUNITY						
EXTREME RURAL!	82.4(5.4) 297.0(3.3)	10.8(4.7) 249.5(4.1)	3.8(1.4) 269.5(6.5)	1.1(0.4) 324.5(13.1)	2.0(1.1) 277.7(6.4)	0.0(0.0) *****(0.0)
DISADVANTAGED URBAN	42.9(10.7) 295.5(5.5)	27.5(7.0) 242.2(5.3)	24.2(5.6) 262.9(4.1)	4.6(1.5) 295.5(10.3)	0.5(0.3) 285.5(13.7)	0.4(0.3) 296.6(12.8)
ADVANTAGED URBAN!	74.4(6.1) 313.4(2.7)	13.5(5.4) 264.2(11.0)	6.6(1.6) 276.4(7.0)	4.7(1.3) 312.0(8.1)	0.8(0.5) 286.6(6.9)	0.0(0.0) *****(0.0)
OTHER	77.1(1.5) 302.5(1.4)	12.4(1.1) 261.8(2.8)	6.2(0.7) 279.0(3.7)	3.6(0.6) 309.7(10.7)	0.5(0.2) 290.6(7.5)	0.1(0.0) 263.7(30.4)
PARENTS' EDUCATION LEVEL						
LESS THAN H.S.	52.9(3.0) 276.3(4.0)	16.6(2.2) 247.8(4.9)	27.2(2.8) 265.2(4.1)	2.6(0.8) 301.4(6.9)	0.5(0.4) 271.5(11.5)	0.2(0.2) 209.5(****)
GRADUATED H.S.	71.7(1.2) 288.7(1.5)	17.4(1.0) 243.9(3.5)	7.9(0.5) 266.0(3.4)	2.1(0.5) 290.5(6.2)	0.8(0.4) 262.9(9.2)	0.0(0.0) 264.7(9.3)
SOME EDUCATION AFTER H.S.	74.9(1.5) 302.3(1.5)	14.7(1.0) 267.0(3.4)	6.9(0.6) 278.9(3.4)	2.5(1.0) 294.9(12.1)	1.0(0.4) 295.7(8.2)	0.0(0.0) *****(0.0)
GRADUATED COLLEGE	78.7(1.0) 314.5(1.2)	10.7(0.8) 266.1(3.1)	4.7(0.5) 287.1(3.9)	5.2(0.4) 319.7(6.4)	0.5(0.2) 298.1(10.4)	0.2(0.1) 294.6(8.4)
UNKNOWN	39.3(6.1) 258.3(7.9)	29.6(5.5) 226.8(9.8)	26.0(4.7) 253.9(12.0)	3.9(1.5) 286.2(11.5)	1.1(1.2) 267.5(2.1)	0.2(0.2) 261.1(23.1)
TYPE OF SCHOOL						
PUBLIC	72.6(0.6) 302.0(1.4)	14.7(0.5) 254.5(2.5)	8.2(0.4) 271.6(2.9)	3.7(0.2) 308.8(7.5)	0.7(0.3) 285.3(4.9)	0.1(0.0) 277.2(18.1)
PRIVATE	78.1(2.6) 306.3(2.9)	10.2(1.7) 280.8(6.0)	8.6(1.9) 279.7(4.5)	2.6(0.6) 300.9(6.7)	0.5(0.3) 292.0(9.3)	0.0(0.0) *****(0.0)
TYPE OF HIGH SCHOOL PROGRAM						
GENERAL	71.1(1.2) 284.7(1.6)	14.0(1.1) 245.3(2.6)	10.4(0.6) 261.2(2.3)	3.5(1.0) 289.5(9.5)	0.9(0.4) 281.0(6.8)	0.2(0.1) 266.9(51.2)
ACADEMIC/COLLEGE PREP	75.8(0.9) 316.6(1.2)	12.9(0.7) 270.3(2.7)	6.8(0.4) 287.4(4.0)	3.9(0.5) 321.0(4.6)	0.5(0.2) 291.3(8.2)	0.1(0.0) 305.4(9.5)
VOCATIONAL/TECHNICAL	67.5(2.4) 274.7(2.8)	22.2(2.4) 235.6(4.1)	7.4(1.2) 258.2(7.2)	1.5(0.3) 271.5(17.4)	1.2(0.4) 284.5(11.9)	0.2(0.3) 251.0(10.6)

The standard errors of the estimated proficiencies appear in parentheses. It can be said with 95 percent certainty that for each population of interest, the value for the whole population is within plus or minus two standard errors of the estimate for the sample.

!Interpret with caution -- the nature of the sample does not allow accurate determination of the variability of this estimated statistic.

	LIFE SCIENCES	PHYSICAL SCIENCES	EARTH AND SPACE SCIENCES	THE NATURE OF SCIENCE
-- TOTAL --	229.0(0.9)	235.5(1.1)	233.6(0.9)	233.5(1.0)
SEX				
MALE	228.8(1.2)	236.9(1.3)	236.7(1.2)	230.8(1.1)
FEMALE	229.2(1.2)	233.9(1.1)	230.2(1.1)	236.3(1.1)
RACE/ETHNICITY				
WHITE	238.0(1.0)	245.4(1.2)	243.1(1.1)	241.6(1.1)
BLACK	203.5(1.6)	206.6(2.0)	203.7(1.5)	212.2(1.7)
HISPANIC	208.6(1.8)	212.8(1.6)	214.8(1.6)	211.7(1.7)
ASIAN/PACIFIC ISLANDER	227.3(4.1)	237.6(3.9)	233.3(3.6)	237.6(3.5)
AMERICAN INDIAN/ ALASKAN NATIVE	221.6(3.8)	228.6(4.0)	228.2(3.6)	226.0(3.8)
REGION				
NORTHEAST	231.1(2.0)	238.9(2.5)	237.0(1.8)	235.1(2.1)
SOUTHEAST	224.1(2.2)	227.8(2.5)	226.1(2.4)	232.7(2.3)
CENTRAL	232.3(2.1)	237.3(2.4)	234.1(2.4)	231.9(2.1)
WEST	228.6(2.1)	237.8(2.2)	236.8(2.1)	234.4(2.0)
TYPE OF COMMUNITY				
EXTREME RURAL	232.9(2.4)	237.4(3.2)	234.7(3.1)	235.0(2.4)
DISADVANTAGED URBAN	204.5(2.8)	211.7(3.0)	208.6(2.7)	211.1(2.4)
ADVANTAGED URBAN	245.2(2.5)	256.1(2.9)	253.7(2.5)	250.9(2.7)
OTHER	229.1(1.1)	235.0(1.2)	233.5(1.1)	233.5(1.2)
PARENTS' EDUCATION LEVEL				
LESS THAN H.S.	218.6(2.7)	223.2(3.3)	221.7(2.7)	223.9(2.3)
GRADUATED H.S.	223.5(1.7)	227.2(1.9)	226.2(1.6)	226.4(1.6)
SOME EDUCATION AFTER H.S.	237.1(2.2)	246.8(2.4)	242.8(2.6)	239.2(1.8)
GRADUATED COLLEGE	238.4(1.3)	245.6(1.5)	243.9(1.3)	243.2(1.4)
UNKNOWN	222.1(0.9)	228.4(1.2)	226.3(0.9)	227.3(1.1)
TYPE OF SCHOOL				
PUBLIC	227.9(1.0)	234.0(1.2)	232.1(1.0)	232.3(1.1)
PRIVATE	237.8(2.1)	247.2(2.2)	245.3(2.1)	243.2(2.0)

The standard errors of the estimated proficiencies appear in parentheses. It can be said with 95 percent certainty that for each population of interest, the value for the whole population is within plus or minus two standard errors of the estimate for the sample.

NAEP 1990 SCIENCE
CROSS-SECTIONAL ASSESSMENT—GRADE 8
Subscale Proficiencies for the Nation
and Demographic Subpopulations

	LIFE SCIENCES	PHYSICAL SCIENCES	EARTH AND SPACE SCIENCES	THE NATURE OF SCIENCE
-- TOTAL --	263.3(1.2)	262.2(1.2)	264.6(1.4)	260.4(1.4)
SEX				
MALE	263.6(1.7)	264.5(1.6)	270.1(1.6)	256.9(1.7)
FEMALE	263.1(1.2)	259.9(1.4)	259.1(1.5)	263.8(1.5)
RACE/ETHNICITY				
WHITE	272.5(1.4)	271.4(1.4)	275.5(1.5)	270.3(1.5)
BLACK	233.2(2.3)	232.4(2.3)	227.9(2.6)	229.7(2.7)
HISPANIC	242.4(2.4)	240.8(2.2)	242.0(2.3)	236.1(2.4)
ASIAN/PACIFIC ISLANDER	272.1(4.0)	270.7(3.9)	269.8(4.3)	267.1(5.2)
AMERICAN INDIAN/ ALASKAN NATIVE!	252.2(9.7)	249.6(7.8)	256.7(7.3)	243.7(15.6)
REGION				
NORTHEAST	267.9(3.0)	270.0(3.3)	270.2(3.6)	267.5(3.8)
SOUTHEAST	256.5(2.1)	255.7(1.7)	257.4(2.3)	253.9(2.2)
CENTRAL	265.3(1.8)	262.9(2.3)	265.8(2.1)	263.0(2.3)
WEST	264.0(3.0)	261.4(2.7)	265.4(3.1)	258.4(2.8)
TYPE OF COMMUNITY				
EXTREME RURAL	257.4(3.4)	256.2(3.1)	260.6(4.1)	251.9(3.7)
DISADVANTAGED URBAN	242.8(3.7)	244.3(4.4)	241.0(4.8)	237.4(4.2)
ADVANTAGED URBAN!	284.6(4.7)	281.8(3.8)	285.0(4.2)	280.0(4.2)
OTHER	263.8(1.3)	262.6(1.5)	265.3(1.7)	261.8(1.6)
PARENTS' EDUCATION LEVEL				
LESS THAN H.S.	241.8(2.8)	239.3(2.4)	243.1(2.7)	238.6(2.4)
GRADUATED H.S.	254.5(1.6)	253.6(1.5)	255.7(1.4)	249.5(1.7)
SOME EDUCATION AFTER H.S.	267.5(1.5)	267.9(1.7)	270.4(1.8)	266.2(1.5)
GRADUATED COLLEGE	276.6(2.0)	275.0(1.8)	278.1(1.7)	275.3(1.8)
UNKNOWN	239.1(2.4)	237.2(2.5)	235.3(2.5)	230.2(2.8)
TYPE OF SCHOOL				
PUBLIC	261.8(1.4)	260.7(1.3)	263.0(1.5)	258.8(1.6)
PRIVATE	274.8(2.1)	274.2(2.0)	276.4(2.0)	272.5(2.8)
ABILITY OF STUDENTS IN CLASS				
HIGH ABILLITY	289.4(2.2)	288.6(2.6)	289.8(2.0)	292.7(2.5)
AVERAGE ABILITY	266.1(1.5)	265.6(1.6)	268.9(1.6)	262.9(1.9)
LOW ABILITY	245.9(3.7)	243.4(4.0)	245.1(4.4)	236.7(4.1)
MIXED ABILITY	262.9(3.1)	261.8(2.7)	266.0(2.9)	261.0(3.2)

The standard errors of the estimated proficiencies appear in parentheses. It can be said with 95 percent certainty that for each population of interest, the value for the whole population is within plus or minus two standard errors of the estimate for the sample.

!Interpret with caution -- the nature of the sample does not allow accurate determination of the variability of this estimated statistic.

	LIFE SCIENCES	PHYSICAL SCIENCES	EARTH AND SPACE SCIENCES	THE NATURE OF SCIENCE
-- TOTAL --	296.1(1.1)	291.0(1.5)	291.1(1.3)	298.5(1.3)
SEX				
MALE	299.4(1.5)	298.5(2.1)	300.3(1.5)	295.8(1.7)
FEMALE	293.0(1.1)	283.9(1.3)	282.5(1.4)	301.0(1.5)
RACE/ETHNICITY				
WHITE	304.5(1.1)	299.8(1.7)	301.4(1.3)	306.6(1.4)
BLACK	262.4(2.0)	253.0(3.1)	247.2(2.8)	266.7(3.0)
HISPANIC	275.1(2.7)	270.5(3.2)	269.5(2.9)	276.5(3.9)
ASIAN/PACIFIC ISLANDER	308.7(7.1)	309.5(8.3)	303.5(6.6)	312.0(6.9)
AMERICAN INDIAN/ ALASKAN NATIVE!	287.0(4.5)	283.3(5.6)	289.2(6.1)	283.0(9.6)
REGION				
NORTHEAST	302.6(2.8)	297.6(3.8)	298.3(3.5)	305.9(3.5)
SOUTHEAST	283.4(2.1)	275.6(3.6)	272.0(2.8)	287.5(2.5)
CENTRAL	298.4(2.0)	292.5(2.6)	294.3(1.8)	297.7(2.9)
WEST	297.7(2.7)	295.1(2.9)	295.7(3.5)	300.8(3.0)
TYPE OF COMMUNITY				
EXTREME RURAL!	294.0(4.1)	287.2(4.0)	288.8(4.0)	295.5(4.4)
DISADVANTAGED URBAN	278.2(4.9)	269.3(5.3)	267.9(7.1)	278.3(4.4)
ADVANTAGED URBAN!	306.2(3.8)	303.2(5.0)	299.6(4.8)	309.1(5.1)
OTHER	298.2(1.4)	293.7(1.9)	294.4(1.7)	301.0(1.6)
PARENTS' EDUCATION LEVEL				
LESS THAN H.S.	274.7(2.8)	265.1(3.0)	263.8(2.7)	274.5(3.0)
GRADUATED H.S.	283.4(1.4)	274.4(1.6)	277.0(1.7)	283.3(1.9)
SOME EDUCATION AFTER H.S.	298.0(1.4)	291.3(1.8)	292.9(1.5)	303.1(1.7)
GRADUATED COLLEGE	308.9(1.3)	307.9(1.8)	305.7(1.8)	311.9(1.6)
UNKNOWN	252.6(4.8)	247.2(6.6)	248.1(6.9)	246.3(5.8)
TYPE OF SCHOOL				
PUBLIC	295.4(1.2)	290.0(1.7)	290.3(1.4)	297.4(1.4)
PRIVATE	302.7(2.9)	299.4(3.2)	297.9(2.6)	308.0(3.0)
TYPE OF HIGH SCHOOL PROGRAM				
GENERAL	281.4(1.4)	272.3(1.7)	275.4(1.6)	280.0(1.7)
ACADEMIC/COLLEGE PREP	309.5(1.2)	307.5(1.6)	305.7(1.4)	315.3(1.4)
VOCATIONAL/TECHNICAL	270.6(2.3)	260.9(3.1)	261.8(3.2)	266.1(2.2)

The standard errors of the estimated proficiencies appear in parentheses. It can be said with 95 percent certainty that for each population of interest, the value for the whole population is within plus or minus two standard errors of the estimate for the sample.

!Interpret with caution -- the nature of the sample does not allow accurate determination of the variability of this estimated statistic.

NAEP 1990 SCIENCE CROSS-SECTIONAL ASSESSMENT
Weighted Percentages of Students
Responding Correctly to Science Items

ITEM DESCRIPTION	GRADE	NATION	MALE	FEMALE	WHITE	BLACK	HISPANIC
CLASSIFY A GRASSHOPPER	4	82.7(1.0)	82.7(1.1)	82.8(1.3)	84.2(1.1)	81.2(2.2)	76.0(2.5)
IDENTIFYING CAT TRACKS	4	83.2(0.8)	81.1(1.1)	85.5(1.1)	86.2(0.9)	74.6(2.1)	76.7(2.3)
GRAPH:MASS OF 4 OBJECTS	4	90.1(0.7)	87.3(1.2)	93.1(0.7)	92.1(0.8)	83.7(1.6)	85.6(1.8)
IDENTIFY A SOLID	4	76.9(0.9)	75.3(1.4)	78.8(1.3)	83.1(0.9)	59.5(2.4)	62.4(2.2)
HUMAN AND DINOSAUR FOSSILS	4	78.5(1.0)	77.0(1.4)	80.1(1.2)	83.7(1.1)	61.2(2.2)	69.8(2.4)
WHICH ARE FOSSILS?	4	61.5(1.1)	61.7(1.8)	61.4(1.3)	67.9(1.4)	43.2(2.1)	47.3(2.2)
TESTING GROWTH OF SEEDS	4	61.9(1.1)	61.7(1.6)	62.0(1.7)	65.2(1.5)	53.3(2.3)	54.3(2.5)
FUNCTION OF LUNGS	4	83.9(0.9)	83.7(1.3)	84.3(1.2)	89.1(1.0)	70.1(2.3)	71.9(2.4)
WHICH IS NOT A LEVER?	4	59.1(1.3)	63.9(1.4)	53.6(1.8)	64.5(1.5)	44.4(2.5)	46.6(3.1)
CLOSEST STAR TO EARTH	4	35.5(1.0)	37.3(1.5)	33.4(1.7)	36.0(1.3)	35.5(2.2)	32.3(2.5)
OBSERVING WITH MICROSCOPE	4	36.9(1.1)	42.9(2.0)	30.3(1.4)	41.3(1.4)	23.3(1.8)	27.9(2.3)
USE LIBRARY FOR WEATHER INFO	4	45.6(1.3)	45.2(1.4)	46.0(2.0)	48.9(1.7)	41.0(2.7)	34.7(2.0)
EXP:TABLET IN HOT/COLD H2O	4	42.4(1.0)	40.9(1.5)	44.2(1.5)	46.5(1.2)	30.7(2.7)	31.4(2.4)
RELATIVE SPEED OF LIGHT	4	44.5(1.4)	51.2(1.6)	37.1(1.8)	49.2(1.6)	28.7(3.2)	32.8(2.5)
FRIDGE-SLOW BACTERIA GROWTH	4	49.7(1.1)	51.0(1.5)	48.3(1.4)	54.1(1.3)	38.3(2.2)	39.9(2.5)
EXP:TEMP PREF OF G'HOPPERS	4	25.5(0.9)	26.2(1.1)	24.8(1.4)	25.8(1.2)	23.2(2.0)	27.1(2.6)
EXAMPLES OF CONDUCTORS	4	62.0(1.1)	66.1(1.3)	57.5(1.6)	66.0(1.4)	44.9(2.5)	58.6(2.4)
DETERMINE WIND DIRECTION	4	28.3(1.1)	25.1(1.3)	31.8(1.6)	30.6(1.4)	17.5(2.0)	25.7(2.1)
CAUSES OF WINDS ON EARTH	4	35.1(1.0)	37.1(1.6)	32.9(1.5)	37.3(1.3)	28.4(2.8)	27.3(2.2)
PREDICT ORDER CANDLES GO OUT	4	33.3(1.1)	37.8(1.4)	28.2(1.6)	36.7(1.5)	23.7(2.1)	24.5(2.4)
BALLOON SHAPE AND VOLUME	4	47.2(1.0)	46.9(1.4)	47.6(1.5)	51.5(1.4)	36.0(2.4)	35.7(2.7)
DETERMINING THE AGE OF A TREE	4	58.9(1.4)	61.3(1.6)	56.3(1.7)	66.7(1.5)	35.5(2.7)	40.3(2.6)
GARDEN LOSES NUTRIENTS	4	45.5(1.2)	46.6(1.7)	44.4(1.6)	51.8(1.5)	26.4(2.2)	28.6(2.7)
LIFE CYCLE OF A BUTTERFLY	4	41.2(1.3)	42.0(2.0)	40.3(1.6)	45.2(1.6)	28.3(2.3)	32.5(2.9)
POSITION OF FULCRUM	4	61.8(1.2)	64.4(1.6)	59.2(1.6)	64.6(1.4)	53.3(2.5)	56.6(2.9)
USE OF A TELESCOPE	4	67.9(0.8)	69.3(1.3)	66.4(1.4)	73.2(1.0)	53.8(2.5)	53.9(2.6)
BALLOON: VOLUME & TEMPERATURE	4	42.1(1.5)	45.1(2.2)	39.0(1.7)	45.2(1.9)	32.3(2.4)	34.3(2.9)

ITEM DESCRIPTION	GRADE	NATION	MALE	FEMALE	WHITE	BLACK	HISPANIC
SUN IS A STAR	4	58.6(1.2)	65.1(1.6)	51.7(1.5)	64.3(1.3)	42.2(2.6)	43.0(2.9)
OBJECTS THAT CONDUCT HEAT	4	48.5(1.1)	48.7(1.5)	48.2(1.4)	52.3(1.4)	35.5(2.9)	38.9(2.8)
PLANTING TO AVOID EROSION	4	30.5(1.0)	30.2(1.6)	30.8(1.4)	31.9(1.3)	27.0(2.6)	28.4(2.7)
LENGTH OF SHADOWS AT NOON	4	34.1(1.0)	38.5(1.5)	29.4(1.3)	37.2(1.3)	23.4(2.1)	27.8(3.3)
READING A HISTOGRAM	4	94.7(0.5)	92.2(0.7)	97.3(0.5)	96.6(0.6)	89.9(1.6)	89.6(1.2)
RELATING SPEED OF CAR/TRAIN	4	44.9(1.0)	48.8(1.7)	40.8(1.4)	49.2(1.2)	30.6(2.2)	37.6(2.7)
CLASSIFYING OBJECTS: SHAPE	4	78.7(1.0)	76.1(1.3)	81.5(1.3)	83.1(1.2)	67.3(2.8)	67.0(2.1)
SURVEY HEIGHT OF BOYS/GIRLS	4	48.5(1.1)	48.0(1.6)	49.0(1.6)	49.6(1.3)	48.1(2.8)	42.0(2.4)
EXAMPLE OF A FORCE	4	63.5(1.0)	61.3(1.4)	65.8(1.5)	69.0(1.3)	49.6(2.7)	50.6(2.2)
	8	82.1(0.7)	78.5(1.1)	85.6(1.0)	83.4(0.7)	82.3(2.6)	71.2(2.5)
FOSSILS SHOW NEW SPECIES	4	68.3(1.1)	67.1(1.4)	69.6(1.2)	72.2(1.4)	58.4(2.2)	58.8(2.3)
	8	83.5(0.9)	81.7(1.3)	85.3(1.1)	87.0(1.1)	74.1(2.8)	74.1(2.4)
ORIGIN OF OIL/COAL	4	22.0(0.9)	25.3(1.4)	18.8(1.3)	22.7(1.2)	18.8(1.8)	20.6(1.7)
	8	50.5(1.4)	60.1(1.8)	40.9(1.6)	55.2(1.6)	34.6(2.5)	41.7(3.0)
ALUMINUM RECYCLING	4	67.3(1.4)	68.0(2.0)	66.5(1.5)	73.9(1.8)	49.3(2.3)	50.2(2.6)
	8	87.6(0.7)	87.0(1.0)	88.3(0.9)	90.4(0.7)	80.2(2.5)	78.7(2.2)
REDUCING ACID RAIN	4	38.0(1.1)	39.1(1.7)	37.0(1.5)	41.4(1.3)	31.2(2.2)	26.7(2.5)
	8	73.3(1.1)	75.6(1.5)	71.1(1.6)	77.3(1.3)	61.1(3.2)	62.4(3.4)
MAJOR TYPES OF ROCKS	4	49.7(1.3)	46.6(1.6)	52.8(2.0)	51.0(1.7)	48.4(2.0)	42.9(2.4)
	8	61.1(1.6)	59.5(1.8)	62.7(1.8)	62.6(1.8)	59.3(3.2)	55.7(3.3)
PREDATOR SKULL	4	61.4(1.0)	66.2(1.3)	56.7(1.4)	65.6(1.2)	50.7(2.3)	51.1(2.5)
	8	68.3(1.1)	75.4(1.1)	61.1(1.6)	73.2(1.1)	53.2(2.8)	59.2(3.1)
GRAPH:HOURS OF DARKNESS	4	36.3(0.8)	37.1(1.3)	35.6(1.3)	39.2(1.1)	26.4(2.0)	31.6(2.4)
	8	71.3(1.1)	70.4(1.4)	72.2(1.5)	75.3(1.2)	57.0(2.9)	64.2(2.2)
GRAPHY:MOST O2 PRODUCED	4	38.4(1.0)	41.6(1.3)	35.3(1.5)	43.2(1.3)	27.6(2.1)	25.2(2.1)
	8	74.2(1.0)	73.5(1.5)	74.9(1.2)	79.7(1.2)	53.8(2.1)	65.2(2.7)
CALCULATE DISTANCE ON MAP	4	46.1(1.2)	48.6(1.7)	43.6(1.7)	51.6(1.6)	29.5(2.0)	36.7(2.7)
	8	76.2(1.0)	77.4(1.3)	75.0(1.5)	80.0(1.1)	64.4(2.6)	68.2(2.3)
TABLE:PLANT GROWTH/LIGHT	4	38.3(1.3)	35.3(1.7)	41.3(1.6)	43.5(1.8)	23.6(2.7)	27.5(2.2)
	8	66.8(0.9)	61.9(1.7)	71.6(1.3)	71.9(1.0)	51.1(3.3)	53.4(2.7)
TABLE:POWDERS X/Y	4	41.9(1.2)	40.8(1.6)	43.0(1.7)	45.0(1.4)	34.3(2.4)	32.8(2.1)
	8	61.4(0.9)	57.8(1.5)	64.9(1.1)	63.8(1.1)	58.3(2.3)	48.4(3.3)
GRAPH:PHOTOSYNTHESIS RATE	4	42.5(1.0)	40.8(1.6)	44.2(1.4)	46.3(1.4)	29.6(2.2)	34.3(2.1)
	8	68.8(1.0)	66.4(1.7)	71.2(1.1)	72.5(1.4)	59.7(2.3)	55.0(2.5)

NAEP 1990 SCIENCE CROSS-SECTIONAL ASSESSMENT
Weighted Percentages of Students
Responding Correctly to Science Items

ITEM DESCRIPTION	GRADE	NATION	MALE	FEMALE	WHITE	BLACK	HISPANIC
WOODPECKER'S BEAK	4	48.8(1.5)	53.7(1.9)	44.0(2.1)	52.7(1.8)	39.4(2.2)	38.8(2.7)
	8	67.9(1.2)	71.9(1.5)	63.8(1.5)	73.7(1.3)	50.2(3.5)	53.7(3.1)
QUESTIONS SCIENCE CAN'T ANSWER	4	37.4(1.0)	38.3(1.5)	36.6(1.4)	39.9(1.3)	29.3(2.1)	33.9(2.8)
	8	66.6(0.9)	62.5(1.4)	70.8(1.2)	70.7(1.1)	54.3(2.8)	55.4(2.4)
EXP:STRONGER OF 2 MAGNETS	4	34.4(1.2)	36.6(1.7)	32.2(1.6)	36.9(1.5)	30.6(2.8)	24.8(2.0)
	8	60.6(1.1)	60.4(1.3)	60.9(1.8)	65.7(1.1)	45.4(3.8)	46.2(2.6)
WATER AND EROSION	4	31.7(1.3)	37.0(1.7)	26.4(1.4)	34.0(1.5)	21.5(2.2)	29.5(2.6)
	8	52.8(1.4)	58.8(1.7)	46.7(2.0)	58.1(1.7)	32.9(3.3)	44.0(3.6)
BLOCK FLOATING IN H2O/OIL	4	28.2(0.9)	27.5(1.2)	29.0(1.5)	30.7(1.3)	21.5(2.4)	22.2(1.9)
	8	38.3(1.0)	37.6(1.3)	39.0(1.5)	40.6(1.1)	33.5(2.4)	30.7(2.0)
EARTH'S TEMP AND SEA LEVEL	4	24.9(1.1)	23.6(1.6)	26.2(1.5)	24.7(1.4)	25.7(2.6)	25.2(2.2)
	8	28.1(1.1)	32.3(1.7)	23.9(1.1)	28.8(1.4)	24.0(2.6)	27.8(2.1)
ANIMALS BREATHE O2	4	84.3(0.9)	83.0(1.3)	85.7(1.1)	88.0(1.3)	74.4(1.8)	75.2(2.3)
	8	94.5(0.6)	94.9(0.8)	94.1(0.7)	96.0(0.6)	88.6(1.9)	91.9(1.5)
CHARACTERISTICS OF A SNAKE	4	72.7(1.1)	74.0(1.4)	71.3(1.5)	75.6(1.4)	63.2(2.6)	67.1(2.2)
	8	82.0(0.8)	81.1(1.1)	82.9(1.1)	83.8(1.0)	78.5(1.8)	74.9(2.1)
INTERPRET FOSSIL TRACKS	4	53.5(1.0)	56.9(1.5)	50.0(1.7)	58.8(1.2)	36.4(2.3)	44.7(2.7)
	8	74.4(1.2)	76.9(1.4)	72.0(1.6)	79.4(1.3)	56.9(2.6)	64.4(2.0)
SEISMOGRAPH'S FUNCTION	4	56.7(1.4)	58.3(1.6)	54.9(1.8)	60.4(1.8)	46.1(2.1)	46.8(3.1)
	8	82.4(1.1)	83.4(1.2)	81.5(1.6)	85.1(1.4)	73.4(2.4)	75.4(2.3)
CLASSIFYING FOSSILS	4	50.0(1.3)	46.4(1.6)	53.7(1.7)	54.2(1.5)	38.2(2.8)	37.9(2.1)
	8	74.0(1.0)	69.2(1.9)	78.7(1.0)	77.4(1.2)	65.2(3.4)	63.9(2.4)
MEASURING RATE OF FLOW	4	42.7(1.3)	43.1(1.4)	42.2(1.9)	47.8(1.6)	27.5(2.2)	28.3(2.4)
	8	71.4(0.9)	69.4(1.7)	73.4(1.1)	75.5(1.1)	59.6(2.7)	56.8(3.3)
WHICH MIXTURE IS SOLUTION?	4	49.5(1.3)	49.7(1.4)	49.3(2.1)	50.5(1.9)	49.1(2.4)	43.8(2.9)
	8	66.9(1.3)	66.0(1.6)	67.8(1.7)	67.7(1.4)	62.9(2.3)	64.9(2.6)
GRAPH:LIGHT PREFERENCE-MOTHS	4	30.4(1.0)	29.5(1.4)	31.3(1.4)	33.5(1.4)	22.4(1.8)	21.9(2.2)
	8	61.0(1.3)	57.1(1.7)	64.8(1.8)	65.0(1.6)	46.8(3.4)	54.9(2.6)
GRAPH:NUMBER OF MOTHS/DAY	4	29.9(1.2)	32.1(1.4)	27.7(1.4)	33.3(1.3)	21.4(1.8)	21.3(2.1)
	8	58.6(1.1)	61.6(1.6)	55.6(1.3)	64.6(1.3)	38.3(2.9)	44.9(3.2)
STARS AND MOON	4	47.9(1.3)	52.2(1.5)	43.7(1.8)	56.0(1.7)	21.0(1.9)	30.7(2.8)
	8	72.6(0.9)	74.1(1.4)	71.2(1.5)	78.9(1.0)	46.5(2.7)	65.4(3.0)
DISSOLVING SUGAR	4	73.1(1.2)	72.0(1.6)	74.1(1.6)	76.8(1.4)	60.4(2.4)	63.0(2.8)
	8	89.3(0.9)	88.2(1.4)	90.4(0.9)	91.4(1.1)	81.8(2.5)	85.1(1.9)
EXPLAIN #11	4	23.8(1.3)	23.8(1.6)	23.8(1.6)	27.6(1.6)	11.0(1.9)	12.9(1.8)
	8	58.4(1.4)	56.3(2.1)	60.3(1.8)	63.9(1.6)	39.0(3.1)	46.7(3.2)

162

NAEP 1990 SCIENCE CROSS-SECTIONAL ASSESSMENT
Weighted Percentages of Students
Responding Correctly to Science Items

ITEM DESCRIPTION	GRADE	NATION	MALE	FEMALE	WHITE	BLACK	HISPANIC
STIRRING SUGAR SOL'N	4	24.0(1.3)	19.1(1.3)	28.9(1.8)	28.0(1.5)	10.4(1.8)	12.6(1.9)
	8	56.4(1.2)	49.6(1.7)	63.0(1.8)	60.3(1.4)	42.3(2.4)	50.6(3.0)
OCEANS CONTAIN MOST H2O	4	76.1(0.9)	78.9(1.4)	73.1(1.3)	80.4(1.2)	59.4(2.3)	71.7(2.2)
	8	85.9(0.9)	88.1(0.9)	83.7(1.4)	87.7(1.1)	76.3(2.6)	86.9(1.8)
NERVES-MESSAGES TO BRAIN	4	59.5(1.3)	61.3(1.9)	57.7(1.4)	65.6(1.6)	39.6(2.4)	49.9(2.5)
	8	85.6(0.8)	86.7(1.0)	84.4(1.1)	88.2(1.1)	76.4(1.9)	80.1(2.8)
SIMPLE FOOD CHAIN	4	58.9(1.3)	60.4(1.6)	57.3(1.5)	64.4(1.6)	42.3(2.3)	48.5(3.0)
	8	80.4(1.2)	83.9(1.2)	76.9(1.8)	85.7(1.3)	62.1(3.4)	70.8(2.4)
OPINION VS. OBSERVATION	4	51.1(1.6)	48.9(2.0)	53.4(2.1)	57.1(2.0)	37.5(3.0)	35.6(2.1)
	8	81.2(1.1)	78.5(1.1)	84.0(1.6)	85.9(1.0)	67.3(3.8)	72.1(2.5)
SOUND TRAVEL THROUGH TABLE	4	57.1(1.2)	52.2(1.6)	62.2(1.7)	61.5(1.5)	42.2(2.1)	48.3(2.3)
	8	75.1(1.1)	72.4(1.3)	77.9(1.5)	78.2(1.1)	60.8(3.6)	74.1(2.8)
LIQUID EXPANDS IN THERMOMETER	4	35.7(1.2)	37.5(1.7)	34.0(1.7)	39.2(1.6)	23.4(1.8)	32.2(2.4)
	8	56.6(1.1)	63.1(1.3)	50.2(1.6)	62.4(1.4)	41.6(3.1)	43.7(2.5)
POSITION OF SHADOW AT 2 PM	4	33.8(1.0)	31.8(1.3)	35.9(1.5)	36.0(1.2)	27.2(1.9)	28.2(2.2)
	8	52.1(1.0)	49.3(1.5)	55.0(1.5)	55.8(1.2)	38.2(2.6)	45.9(2.8)
OBSERVATION:DUCKS FEEDING	4	36.1(1.0)	37.7(1.6)	34.4(1.6)	39.0(1.2)	27.4(2.4)	30.4(2.6)
	8	57.3(1.2)	55.1(1.7)	59.6(1.6)	62.6(1.2)	47.6(3.2)	40.0(2.6)
STEPS TO IDENTIFY MINERALS	4	35.3(1.1)	34.9(1.3)	35.8(1.6)	37.3(1.4)	30.5(3.0)	30.1(2.3)
	8	62.1(1.3)	59.2(1.6)	65.1(1.8)	66.5(1.5)	52.9(3.6)	47.2(3.3)
BATTERY/BULB	4	3.7(0.6)	6.3(1.1)	1.1(0.4)	4.5(0.8)	0.0(0.0)	2.2(1.0)
	8	11.0(0.7)	19.7(1.3)	2.3(0.3)	12.3(1.0)	6.2(1.2)	10.3(1.7)
SEPARATE IRON FILINGS	4	32.3(1.3)	36.1(1.6)	28.5(1.7)	38.4(1.7)	14.0(2.1)	16.8(2.3)
	8	59.9(1.2)	62.1(1.6)	57.6(1.8)	67.9(1.3)	35.1(2.8)	41.7(3.5)
SEPARATE SAND/SALT	4	0.1(0.0)	0.1(0.1)	0.1(0.1)	0.1(0.1)	0.0(0.0)	0.0(0.0)
	8	3.1(0.4)	3.7(0.6)	2.4(0.5)	3.8(0.5)	0.5(0.3)	1.3(0.6)
POSITIONS OF STARS	4	55.6(1.0)	54.4(1.7)	56.8(1.5)	62.3(1.1)	31.0(2.5)	45.5(2.0)
	8	72.2(1.0)	73.4(1.4)	70.9(1.5)	77.3(1.1)	54.1(2.7)	63.9(2.8)
	12	82.7(0.9)	84.2(1.2)	81.3(1.3)	86.0(1.0)	67.3(2.9)	79.8(2.9)
WATER-FREEZING TEMP	4	55.1(1.4)	53.0(1.6)	57.3(1.9)	56.4(1.9)	53.5(2.5)	49.5(2.8)
	8	53.2(1.2)	54.0(1.4)	52.3(1.9)	53.2(1.2)	54.0(3.4)	50.1(2.3)
	12	52.6(1.3)	55.5(1.9)	49.9(1.5)	53.9(1.5)	44.6(3.0)	49.6(3.8)
FOSSILS AND EARTH'S AGE	4	61.1(1.3)	59.4(1.5)	62.9(1.7)	65.5(1.6)	49.1(2.4)	48.2(2.3)
	8	80.2(0.9)	76.9(1.5)	83.4(0.9)	83.7(0.9)	71.0(2.6)	69.8(2.3)
	12	89.8(0.8)	87.8(1.1)	91.7(0.8)	91.8(0.8)	82.4(2.1)	85.3(2.8)
TABLE:PROPERTIES OF SUGAR	4	58.9(1.0)	56.3(1.4)	61.5(1.6)	63.9(1.3)	43.9(2.6)	46.0(2.2)
	8	83.0(0.7)	81.5(1.0)	84.4(1.1)	85.3(0.9)	77.1(2.2)	75.8(2.7)
	12	87.7(0.7)	86.3(1.1)	89.0(1.0)	88.8(0.8)	82.4(2.4)	84.3(1.9)

ITEM DESCRIPTION	GRADE	NATION	MALE	FEMALE	WHITE	BLACK	HISPANIC
EXP:WATER EVAPORATION	4	56.2(1.0)	51.7(1.4)	60.9(1.9)	61.7(1.3)	40.7(3.6)	41.8(2.5)
	8	76.4(0.9)	72.3(1.4)	80.3(1.0)	80.2(1.0)	62.5(3.4)	68.7(2.2)
	12	89.3(0.6)	86.5(1.1)	91.9(0.7)	91.8(0.8)	79.4(2.1)	81.5(2.7)
INHERITANCE/CAT'S TAILS	4	43.1(1.2)	42.8(1.6)	43.4(1.4)	47.7(1.5)	29.8(2.4)	30.6(2.3)
	8	70.8(1.1)	71.0(1.5)	70.5(1.3)	76.8(1.3)	51.9(3.1)	59.5(2.5)
	12	86.1(0.8)	84.9(1.3)	87.2(0.9)	89.9(0.9)	68.5(2.4)	80.4(3.6)
DINOSAUR/FISH EVOLUTION	4	51.5(0.9)	54.0(1.6)	48.9(1.6)	55.0(1.3)	40.8(2.9)	44.7(2.4)
	8	65.8(1.2)	69.9(1.6)	61.7(1.6)	69.1(1.4)	51.8(3.8)	62.1(2.6)
	12	76.7(1.0)	80.7(1.3)	72.9(1.3)	79.7(1.3)	59.3(3.4)	79.0(2.5)
CONTINENTS' POSITIONS CHANGE	4	42.9(1.2)	42.5(1.5)	43.3(1.7)	45.2(1.5)	36.0(3.0)	37.9(2.5)
	8	63.9(1.3)	66.4(1.6)	61.5(1.5)	68.9(1.3)	47.1(2.7)	52.9(3.0)
	12	73.5(1.3)	77.3(1.9)	70.0(1.5)	77.3(1.5)	55.0(3.0)	67.0(3.5)
HEART AND EXERCISE	4	40.4(1.1)	39.7(1.5)	41.1(1.4)	42.8(1.4)	33.7(2.3)	34.0(2.2)
	8	63.1(1.0)	63.1(1.3)	63.1(1.6)	68.2(1.2)	48.6(2.4)	49.3(3.5)
	12	72.9(1.1)	72.9(1.5)	73.0(1.3)	76.0(1.4)	59.7(3.0)	65.4(3.6)
TIME BETWEEN LIGHTNING/THUNDER	4	35.7(1.2)	37.5(1.4)	33.8(1.7)	39.7(1.5)	23.9(2.1)	27.0(1.9)
	8	61.9(1.0)	63.5(1.5)	60.4(1.6)	69.4(1.1)	41.8(2.6)	44.7(2.9)
	12	78.6(1.1)	80.7(1.3)	76.6(1.3)	84.4(1.1)	58.8(2.9)	60.8(3.5)
DIRECTION OF SUNRISE/SUNSET	4	37.9(1.0)	39.8(1.5)	35.9(1.6)	41.0(1.5)	31.5(2.4)	26.0(2.2)
	8	55.5(0.9)	60.2(1.3)	51.0(1.6)	61.7(1.2)	40.3(3.5)	38.2(2.3)
	12	73.8(0.9)	78.8(1.0)	69.1(1.3)	80.4(0.8)	53.7(3.6)	48.8(3.3)
COOLING AND CONDENSATION	4	34.7(1.2)	35.6(1.7)	33.7(1.6)	34.7(1.4)	38.3(2.0)	31.4(2.2)
	8	49.3(1.2)	52.7(1.5)	45.9(1.6)	52.9(1.4)	38.1(3.0)	41.9(2.8)
	12	61.7(1.0)	68.2(1.3)	55.6(1.8)	65.6(1.2)	43.3(2.4)	50.7(3.8)
SCI KNOWLEDGE-OBSERVATION	4	46.6(1.3)	44.6(1.9)	48.7(1.6)	49.8(1.7)	38.9(1.8)	34.8(2.5)
	8	73.9(0.8)	69.2(1.3)	78.5(0.9)	77.6(1.0)	63.1(2.7)	62.7(2.5)
	12	85.9(0.9)	82.4(1.3)	89.1(1.0)	87.5(1.0)	76.3(2.4)	84.7(2.5)
TABLE:MELTING POINTS	4	48.8(1.1)	51.4(1.6)	46.3(1.6)	52.7(1.5)	38.1(2.9)	39.6(2.2)
	8	72.2(0.8)	75.4(1.3)	69.0(1.5)	76.4(1.1)	60.1(2.5)	61.4(2.6)
	12	80.9(0.9)	83.7(1.1)	78.3(1.2)	84.6(1.0)	65.4(3.0)	72.8(3.5)
ENERGY FLOW IN FOOD WEB	4	37.1(1.1)	39.4(1.7)	34.8(1.3)	38.5(1.5)	31.8(2.4)	34.1(2.2)
	8	55.6(1.1)	56.2(1.4)	55.1(1.6)	59.7(1.4)	46.6(2.5)	41.7(2.6)
	12	70.5(0.8)	71.0(1.3)	70.0(1.1)	74.1(1.0)	58.3(3.1)	58.7(3.1)
LAND/H2O TEMP DIFFERENCE	4	34.1(1.2)	35.7(1.6)	32.4(1.7)	34.7(1.5)	35.7(2.6)	29.3(2.2)
	8	46.5(1.3)	47.7(1.8)	45.4(1.5)	50.2(1.5)	35.5(2.8)	37.8(3.0)
	12	59.8(1.3)	63.7(1.6)	56.2(1.4)	63.7(1.5)	46.4(3.4)	50.1(3.4)
EXP:PLANT FERTILIZER	4	36.4(1.2)	35.0(1.6)	37.9(1.9)	39.2(1.3)	29.6(3.0)	26.9(2.4)
	8	62.6(1.1)	62.2(1.4)	62.9(1.5)	67.0(1.1)	48.7(3.7)	53.4(2.2)
	12	78.4(0.9)	77.4(1.4)	79.4(1.2)	81.5(1.1)	64.1(2.7)	71.2(2.9)
VOLCANOS AND IGNEOUS ROCKS	4	28.8(1.1)	31.3(1.8)	26.2(1.2)	28.8(1.5)	28.7(2.4)	27.8(2.2)
	8	36.3(1.1)	36.7(1.5)	36.0(1.3)	37.8(1.1)	33.0(2.7)	28.7(2.6)
	12	32.6(0.8)	34.5(1.6)	30.8(1.3)	34.4(0.9)	26.3(2.8)	24.7(3.2)

NAEP 1990 SCIENCE CROSS-SECTIONAL ASSESSMENT
Weighted Percentages of Students
Responding Correctly to Science Items

ITEM DESCRIPTION	GRADE	NATION	MALE	FEMALE	WHITE	BLACK	HISPANIC
HYPOTHESIS-IDEAS TO BE TESTED	4	26.7(1.1)	26.8(1.5)	26.5(1.5)	27.5(1.5)	23.1(2.1)	23.3(2.7)
	8	62.8(1.3)	59.8(2.0)	65.7(1.6)	67.9(1.6)	49.6(3.6)	47.4(2.7)
	12	74.5(0.9)	72.8(1.3)	76.0(1.3)	78.1(1.2)	64.9(2.7)	60.6(2.7)
DIAGRAM:LEAF'S FUNCTION	4	19.3(0.9)	21.1(1.3)	17.4(1.4)	19.7(1.1)	17.7(1.9)	17.9(2.0)
	8	23.4(1.2)	29.4(1.7)	17.5(1.3)	25.4(1.3)	16.5(2.3)	18.3(1.9)
	12	29.8(1.1)	37.1(1.6)	23.0(1.4)	31.9(1.2)	22.7(2.4)	18.0(3.1)
DIAGRAM:FLOWER'S FUNCTION	4	22.6(1.0)	24.3(1.5)	20.7(1.3)	24.4(1.2)	15.6(1.7)	16.5(1.5)
	8	36.4(1.1)	39.4(1.4)	33.6(1.5)	41.1(1.4)	22.6(2.2)	21.7(2.1)
	12	52.0(1.3)	54.4(1.3)	49.9(1.9)	55.9(1.3)	32.6(3.6)	42.1(4.3)
FORCE ON ROCK	4	60.5(1.2)	66.9(1.6)	53.7(1.8)	65.3(1.4)	47.5(3.2)	46.9(2.4)
	8	80.2(0.9)	85.4(1.0)	75.1(1.3)	85.1(1.0)	64.6(2.6)	70.2(2.1)
	12	83.9(1.0)	87.9(1.0)	80.1(1.5)	87.7(0.8)	65.7(3.3)	83.1(2.1)
LIGHT HITS MIRROR	4	35.7(1.1)	44.2(1.7)	26.9(1.5)	41.0(1.3)	18.3(1.6)	25.6(2.2)
	8	62.6(1.2)	72.7(1.2)	52.3(1.8)	69.0(1.3)	37.2(3.0)	53.1(2.7)
	12	65.9(1.2)	75.1(1.7)	57.1(1.4)	71.5(1.3)	43.2(2.9)	55.4(3.4)
FALLING GLASSES	4	32.7(1.3)	35.7(1.7)	29.7(1.7)	35.8(1.7)	21.5(2.7)	29.9(2.5)
	8	40.6(1.1)	45.2(1.6)	35.9(1.6)	42.4(1.1)	35.0(2.8)	37.9(2.6)
	12	41.9(1.1)	50.6(1.5)	33.6(1.5)	46.1(1.3)	25.2(3.3)	32.8(3.3)
THERMOMETER	4	10.9(0.7)	12.8(1.0)	8.8(0.9)	12.9(0.9)	6.0(1.1)	6.2(1.1)
	8	46.9(1.2)	49.6(1.7)	44.2(1.6)	52.1(1.5)	28.9(3.0)	36.2(2.2)
	12	66.2(1.1)	71.7(1.6)	61.1(1.4)	70.2(1.3)	49.6(2.1)	56.2(4.2)
HALF MOON	4	12.1(1.0)	12.4(1.2)	11.9(1.2)	14.3(1.2)	5.4(1.3)	6.9(1.2)
	8	28.9(0.9)	31.6(1.1)	26.2(1.4)	33.2(1.2)	16.5(2.7)	15.7(1.6)
	12	42.2(1.1)	49.4(1.4)	35.4(1.4)	47.9(1.3)	15.4(2.2)	31.6(2.9)
SOLAR ECLIPSE	4	26.0(1.2)	33.0(1.6)	18.8(1.6)	30.9(1.4)	10.5(1.5)	15.0(2.2)
	8	54.4(1.2)	63.6(1.6)	45.1(1.6)	61.3(1.4)	29.8(3.1)	41.5(2.2)
	12	66.5(1.3)	78.8(1.5)	54.9(1.7)	73.0(1.6)	33.8(2.7)	57.6(3.8)
X-SEC OF WORM	4	14.7(0.9)	13.5(1.1)	15.9(1.4)	16.4(1.1)	10.4(1.4)	9.5(1.8)
	8	29.1(1.2)	29.6(1.3)	28.6(1.6)	31.3(1.3)	23.7(3.2)	23.9(2.3)
	12	41.6(1.3)	46.3(2.0)	37.1(1.4)	44.7(1.5)	27.1(2.7)	32.7(2.8)
PATH OF OBJECT	4	2.7(0.5)	3.7(0.7)	1.7(0.5)	3.1(0.6)	0.1(0.1)	3.3(1.1)
	8	6.1(0.5)	9.1(0.9)	3.0(0.5)	7.0(0.6)	3.8(1.5)	3.8(1.2)
	12	16.0(0.6)	22.8(1.4)	9.6(0.8)	18.5(0.8)	3.3(0.9)	9.2(2.5)
PATH OF BALL FROM TUBE	4	28.2(1.3)	35.6(1.9)	20.9(1.5)	31.0(1.8)	19.3(1.7)	21.3(2.1)
	8	46.6(1.0)	56.7(1.5)	36.5(1.2)	50.5(1.3)	32.1(3.0)	43.0(2.5)
	12	57.8(1.0)	70.7(1.3)	45.7(1.3)	61.6(1.1)	38.7(3.0)	52.3(3.0)
PREDATOR/PREY GRAPH	4	11.7(0.8)	13.2(1.1)	10.2(1.2)	13.6(0.9)	5.6(2.0)	6.1(1.8)
	8	42.8(1.2)	46.6(1.5)	38.9(1.4)	48.2(1.6)	23.6(3.1)	27.5(2.9)
	12	64.9(1.1)	70.5(1.1)	59.6(1.4)	71.3(1.0)	35.9(3.1)	45.8(3.5)
FINDING CAUSE OF A SORE THROAT	4	41.8(1.1)	36.3(1.5)	47.5(1.6)	46.7(1.3)	25.9(2.3)	35.0(2.5)
	8	68.7(1.0)	62.1(1.6)	75.5(1.3)	72.4(1.2)	58.6(2.8)	56.9(3.3)
	12	84.0(0.7)	79.1(1.2)	88.6(0.8)	87.3(0.9)	72.2(2.2)	76.3(3.3)

NAEP 1990 SCIENCE CROSS-SECTIONAL ASSESSMENT
Weighted Percentages of Students
Responding Correctly to Science Items

ITEM DESCRIPTION	GRADE	NATION	MALE	FEMALE	WHITE	BLACK	HISPANIC
PLANTS BEND TOWARD LIGHT	4	27.3(1.0)	28.4(1.6)	26.3(1.4)	28.7(1.2)	20.5(2.1)	26.8(2.5)
	8	55.1(1.3)	59.6(1.7)	50.6(1.7)	60.4(1.4)	35.3(3.5)	47.5(2.8)
	12	64.4(1.2)	67.0(1.6)	62.2(1.8)	69.3(1.5)	42.3(3.0)	55.9(3.6)
HEIGHT OF CHILDREN IN 1902/197	8	70.1(0.9)	68.2(1.4)	72.0(1.6)	74.4(1.1)	55.3(2.6)	59.0(2.8)
BEST TEMP FOR IVY GROWTH	8	46.8(1.3)	45.5(1.6)	48.0(1.6)	48.9(1.5)	39.2(2.6)	39.7(3.3)
EFFECT OF TEMP ON BALL'S BOUNC	8	48.8(1.2)	46.5(1.6)	51.0(1.6)	52.1(1.4)	37.9(2.8)	38.8(2.0)
HOW MEASURE # OF SNOWFLAKES	8	62.1(1.0)	59.4(1.5)	64.8(1.7)	64.4(1.2)	54.3(3.1)	54.8(2.6)
HOW REPORT # OF SNOWFLAKES	8	36.5(1.1)	36.4(1.7)	36.5(1.3)	39.1(1.4)	26.3(3.3)	32.6(2.5)
CAUSE OF OCEAN TIDES	8	52.5(1.5)	58.6(1.6)	46.4(2.0)	58.3(1.9)	31.5(2.8)	38.5(2.5)
MEANING OF SPECIFIC HEAT	8	15.7(0.6)	18.0(1.2)	13.4(0.9)	15.8(0.8)	15.7(2.4)	14.0(1.9)
NRG SOURCE FOR PHOTOSYNTHESIS	8	77.8(1.2)	77.8(1.6)	77.9(1.4)	80.6(1.4)	66.4(3.4)	72.4(2.4)
MIXING RED/GREEN LIGHT	8	46.8(1.3)	42.0(1.8)	51.5(1.8)	47.5(1.6)	47.6(3.2)	41.6(2.6)
HYPOTHESIS:RIVER'S WATER LEVEL	8	37.1(1.3)	36.0(1.7)	38.1(1.7)	38.2(1.5)	37.9(3.5)	29.5(2.2)
GRAVITY AND 2 OBJECTS' MASS	8	35.7(1.1)	38.2(1.5)	33.3(1.7)	37.0(1.4)	32.8(2.5)	32.1(2.4)
ICE CAPS NOT ON MOON'S SURFACE	8	54.2(1.3)	58.8(1.6)	49.8(1.7)	58.2(1.5)	38.7(3.7)	49.2(2.3)
CAUSE OF CHANGING SEASONS	8	70.7(1.2)	69.3(1.6)	72.0(1.5)	74.5(1.2)	67.7(3.9)	52.8(3.3)
LIVING/MADE OF CELLS	8	81.2(0.8)	79.9(1.1)	82.5(1.3)	83.7(0.9)	72.5(2.8)	77.3(1.8)
EXP:FOOD PREF OF RABBITS	8	46.5(1.1)	46.6(1.8)	46.3(1.4)	45.8(1.4)	47.5(2.5)	49.3(2.7)
STAR FORMATION IN JAPAN	8	30.5(1.0)	31.6(1.6)	29.3(1.2)	30.3(1.0)	28.0(2.0)	32.0(2.8)
BEST WAY TO SURVEY STUDENTS	8	43.3(1.2)	40.2(1.7)	46.4(1.5)	46.2(1.4)	31.8(2.8)	38.2(2.7)
MUSEUM: HABITATS	8	68.8(1.3)	62.6(1.8)	75.1(1.5)	72.5(1.6)	55.0(3.5)	59.1(2.6)
MUSEUM: SIMILAR ANIMALS	8	54.5(1.2)	51.7(1.8)	57.4(1.4)	57.4(1.4)	44.7(3.3)	45.9(2.5)
WOLVES AND CARIBOU	8	37.4(1.1)	40.4(1.9)	34.3(1.4)	41.4(1.3)	22.0(2.2)	25.1(2.4)
CELLS, TISSUES, ORGANS	8	39.3(1.0)	39.2(1.5)	39.5(1.3)	43.0(1.3)	28.5(2.2)	27.8(2.4)
PRESENT ENERGY SOURCE IN U.S.	8	44.3(1.0)	46.8(1.8)	41.7(1.6)	49.0(1.4)	30.2(2.6)	26.3(2.2)
ACCELERATION OF BALL ON RAMP	8	56.3(1.0)	59.7(1.5)	52.9(1.7)	60.7(1.1)	41.9(2.9)	46.5(3.1)
PREDICTING SNOWFALL	8	55.6(1.2)	53.6(1.9)	57.5(1.2)	60.0(1.5)	40.9(2.7)	42.1(2.6)
HUMAN ERROR IN MEASURING TIME	8	37.9(1.1)	43.0(1.4)	32.6(1.4)	40.7(1.3)	28.8(2.6)	30.8(2.7)

NAEP 1990 SCIENCE CROSS-SECTIONAL ASSESSMENT
Weighted Percentages of Students
Responding Correctly to Science Items

ITEM DESCRIPTION	GRADE	NATION	MALE	FEMALE	WHITE	BLACK	HISPANIC
SEASONAL RAINFALL GRAPH	8	37.3(1.0)	37.2(1.5)	37.5(1.2)	39.7(1.2)	31.2(2.6)	29.4(2.6)
OBJECT WITH MOST INERTIA	8	39.3(1.1)	44.0(1.7)	34.8(1.2)	42.7(1.2)	28.9(2.8)	28.3(2.2)
	12	50.7(1.1)	61.3(1.6)	40.9(1.5)	54.8(1.3)	35.2(2.7)	39.6(4.8)
EXP:APPROPRIATE CONTROLS	8	41.2(1.1)	40.8(1.4)	41.5(1.6)	43.4(1.5)	32.2(2.3)	36.6(2.1)
	12	59.4(1.2)	57.7(1.9)	61.0(1.4)	64.7(1.6)	36.8(2.1)	48.0(3.6)
EVIDENCE THAT LIGHT IS ENERGY	8	58.9(1.1)	61.3(1.5)	56.5(1.7)	62.9(1.3)	44.2(3.3)	49.9(2.5)
	12	75.0(1.1)	77.5(1.6)	72.6(1.4)	78.7(1.0)	61.8(3.5)	64.0(4.2)
SALT LEFT AFTER EVAPORATION	8	23.6(0.9)	25.5(1.6)	21.8(1.3)	24.2(1.1)	22.0(2.2)	20.6(2.2)
	12	34.6(1.1)	39.1(1.4)	30.4(1.2)	37.7(1.3)	21.3(2.8)	25.6(3.2)
ESTIMATED AGE OF EARTH	8	23.8(1.0)	24.2(1.5)	23.4(1.5)	25.4(1.2)	16.0(2.1)	22.3(2.4)
	12	32.3(1.1)	34.5(1.8)	30.3(1.2)	34.0(1.2)	22.2(2.8)	27.9(2.6)
OBSERVING SPIDER AND WEB	8	54.7(1.2)	54.8(1.6)	54.5(1.5)	61.2(1.5)	35.5(2.4)	40.3(2.8)
	12	72.8(1.3)	74.4(1.4)	71.4(1.7)	78.6(1.3)	51.2(3.9)	56.6(3.8)
EXP:MEASURE VINE GROWTH	8	57.6(1.1)	55.2(1.4)	60.1(1.6)	60.2(1.4)	47.9(2.7)	52.8(2.6)
	12	67.0(1.1)	66.2(1.6)	67.8(1.6)	68.9(1.3)	60.5(3.0)	60.3(2.8)
MEASURE MASS WITH SPRING SCALE	8	64.6(1.1)	62.0(1.5)	67.2(1.7)	69.0(1.3)	53.5(3.3)	49.2(3.1)
	12	76.4(1.0)	77.9(1.3)	74.9(1.3)	78.5(1.2)	68.3(2.8)	69.3(2.6)
EXP DESIGN:CONTROL LIGHT	8	72.1(0.9)	67.6(1.2)	76.7(1.2)	74.6(1.0)	66.8(2.6)	62.9(3.3)
	12	80.8(1.1)	78.5(1.1)	83.0(1.6)	83.6(1.2)	71.6(3.1)	70.4(3.9)
EXP DESIGN:APPLY FERTILIZER	8	50.3(1.0)	48.1(1.4)	52.6(1.8)	56.2(1.3)	30.3(2.0)	38.3(3.0)
	12	68.8(1.3)	68.3(1.7)	69.3(1.6)	75.0(1.3)	43.9(3.2)	53.1(3.4)
EXP DESIGN:SAMPLE SIZE	8	27.0(1.1)	31.1(1.5)	22.9(1.5)	31.0(1.4)	15.3(2.3)	17.5(2.3)
	12	46.3(1.4)	53.9(1.7)	39.0(1.7)	53.3(1.5)	20.0(2.6)	27.9(3.1)
HYPOTHESIS:SALT/CONTAINER	8	49.7(1.4)	51.5(1.5)	47.9(1.9)	52.7(1.7)	38.0(2.7)	44.7(2.7)
	12	66.5(0.9)	68.0(1.5)	65.0(1.4)	68.4(1.0)	58.9(2.7)	59.9(3.2)
MEASURE ANGLE OF POLARIS	8	56.3(1.3)	53.5(1.7)	59.2(1.4)	58.9(1.2)	48.2(3.5)	53.2(3.6)
	12	64.5(1.0)	62.9(1.4)	66.1(1.8)	64.7(1.3)	65.3(3.2)	61.8(2.7)
EARTH'S TEMP FROM CORE TO CRUS	8	38.3(1.2)	40.1(1.6)	36.5(1.7)	44.2(1.4)	18.5(2.3)	29.0(2.9)
	12	51.3(1.1)	53.5(1.6)	49.2(1.7)	56.2(1.2)	31.5(2.4)	39.3(3.7)
DINOSAUR EXTINCTION	8	49.0(1.4)	49.6(1.8)	48.3(1.7)	51.8(1.7)	38.5(2.9)	41.5(2.4)
	12	60.2(1.3)	65.0(1.7)	55.6(1.8)	63.2(1.5)	42.1(2.6)	59.2(3.3)
WET/DRY BULB:MEAURE RH	8	37.9(1.1)	39.5(1.4)	36.3(1.9)	39.8(1.4)	30.7(3.0)	34.4(2.3)
	12	53.2(1.4)	55.5(1.7)	51.1(1.6)	57.0(1.7)	38.2(2.7)	44.5(3.7)
WET/DRY BULB:EFFECT OF TEMP	8	39.1(1.0)	40.4(1.4)	37.8(1.4)	39.4(1.3)	40.7(2.9)	37.2(3.3)
	12	49.0(1.1)	51.2(1.8)	47.0(1.5)	52.6(1.3)	33.4(2.6)	42.2(2.7)

NAEP 1990 SCIENCE CROSS-SECTIONAL ASSESSMENT
Weighted Percentages of Students
Responding Correctly to Science Items

ITEM DESCRIPTION	GRADE	NATION	MALE	FEMALE	WHITE	BLACK	HISPANIC
EXP:COMPARE EATING RATES	8	29.2(0.9)	28.7(1.3)	29.8(1.1)	31.4(1.2)	26.3(2.3)	21.2(2.1)
	12	39.9(1.1)	39.5(1.4)	40.4(1.5)	43.0(1.4)	29.7(2.2)	28.1(3.0)
NE WIND BLOWS TOWARD SW	8	32.8(1.0)	38.2(1.4)	27.3(1.4)	35.6(1.2)	23.7(2.0)	24.1(2.1)
	12	47.5(1.3)	54.3(1.7)	41.0(1.8)	53.2(1.5)	24.2(2.5)	34.1(2.9)
DIAGRAM OF FOLDED MTS	8	44.0(1.7)	47.4(1.8)	40.5(2.3)	47.5(2.2)	33.7(3.2)	35.7(3.5)
	12	48.5(1.2)	53.8(1.2)	43.4(1.9)	51.1(1.4)	35.1(2.2)	46.6(3.4)
EXP:MOISTURE PREF OF INSECTS	8	41.5(1.0)	41.5(1.4)	41.4(1.3)	44.2(1.2)	31.9(2.7)	36.7(2.1)
	12	57.4(1.2)	59.1(1.6)	55.9(1.5)	60.2(1.4)	45.7(3.2)	52.6(3.0)
VOLUME OF SPACE BETWEEN ROCKS	8	38.5(1.2)	40.4(1.4)	36.5(1.8)	41.2(1.5)	27.2(2.6)	33.3(2.9)
	12	53.9(1.3)	56.8(1.7)	51.2(1.7)	56.7(1.5)	37.6(2.8)	49.9(3.1)
RELATIVE AGE OF ROCK LAYERS	8	26.7(1.1)	25.3(1.2)	28.1(1.7)	30.0(1.4)	16.8(2.0)	18.5(2.4)
	12	38.9(1.2)	37.6(1.7)	40.1(1.5)	42.8(1.3)	22.1(2.8)	25.7(3.0)
DETERMINE BEST ELECTROLYTE	8	20.6(0.9)	20.5(1.2)	20.8(1.4)	22.5(1.1)	13.2(1.9)	15.8(2.4)
	12	28.2(1.3)	30.6(1.7)	26.0(1.5)	30.7(1.5)	17.8(2.7)	21.6(3.2)
INTERPRET GRAPH:DINOSAURS	8	26.7(1.1)	28.3(1.6)	24.9(1.6)	26.8(1.2)	25.2(3.1)	27.4(3.4)
	12	27.8(1.2)	33.5(1.7)	22.5(1.4)	28.2(1.3)	25.1(2.3)	28.8(3.8)
BEST BATTERY	8	66.5(1.1)	68.5(1.3)	64.5(1.6)	68.2(1.1)	58.5(3.6)	60.4(3.0)
	12	69.6(1.2)	68.9(1.7)	70.2(1.5)	71.8(1.4)	63.0(3.6)	58.9(2.7)
HOW TO USE INFO	8	60.9(1.6)	59.5(2.0)	62.4(1.8)	64.4(1.8)	47.4(3.0)	47.0(3.0)
	12	70.8(1.3)	69.2(1.8)	72.2(1.5)	74.5(1.4)	54.0(4.6)	59.5(4.1)
ENERGY FROM BATTERY	8	4.8(0.9)	5.5(1.1)	4.0(1.0)	5.3(1.1)	3.0(1.3)	0.8(0.7)
	12	11.5(1.1)	16.6(1.9)	6.7(0.9)	12.8(1.2)	4.0(1.4)	10.7(3.2)
TEMPERATURE GRAPH	8	65.9(1.3)	64.8(1.4)	67.0(2.0)	68.8(1.5)	58.3(4.1)	55.2(2.9)
	12	77.8(1.2)	80.9(1.5)	74.9(1.6)	81.0(1.2)	64.3(3.2)	64.8(5.0)
IMAGE ON RETINA	8	32.9(1.0)	40.2(1.6)	25.7(1.3)	37.2(1.2)	13.3(2.0)	25.8(3.3)
	12	42.2(1.3)	53.2(1.7)	31.8(1.6)	45.4(1.5)	24.3(3.8)	32.3(4.4)
EARTH'S CRUST MOTION	8	13.8(0.9)	15.8(1.2)	11.9(1.2)	15.3(1.2)	4.7(1.6)	12.7(2.0)
	12	14.8(0.9)	15.9(1.2)	13.8(1.2)	15.9(1.0)	11.0(2.3)	10.2(2.8)
BLOOD FLOW IN HEART	8	15.1(1.1)	18.2(1.7)	11.9(1.2)	17.4(1.4)	7.0(1.8)	7.9(1.9)
	12	24.5(1.0)	30.9(1.5)	18.6(1.2)	26.6(1.2)	13.1(2.1)	16.6(3.0)
OBSERVING A SEALED AQUARIUM	8	54.3(1.1)	54.5(1.3)	54.0(1.6)	56.9(1.1)	45.5(3.2)	49.8(2.8)
	12	70.8(0.9)	71.2(1.5)	70.5(1.4)	73.8(1.1)	59.5(3.1)	60.2(3.7)
TISSUES AND CELLS	8	57.0(1.4)	60.1(1.5)	53.8(1.7)	59.6(1.8)	48.1(2.8)	47.9(2.7)
	12	63.1(1.2)	64.6(1.7)	61.7(1.4)	65.2(1.5)	54.7(2.0)	56.3(3.8)
MELTING CRUSHED ICE	8	44.3(1.1)	48.3(1.5)	40.3(1.5)	48.8(1.4)	28.0(2.3)	34.7(2.5)
	12	59.3(1.2)	66.1(1.5)	53.1(1.6)	65.0(1.5)	33.7(2.8)	49.9(4.3)

168

Weighted Percentages of Students
Responding Correctly to Science Items

ITEM DESCRIPTION	GRADE	NATION	MALE	FEMALE	WHITE	BLACK	HISPANIC
SULFUR DIOXIDE AND ACID RAIN	8	55.3(1.1)	59.5(1.6)	51.1(1.7)	58.9(1.3)	46.2(2.6)	40.9(3.3)
	12	66.6(1.2)	74.7(1.4)	59.2(1.7)	70.8(1.5)	50.6(2.8)	56.7(4.5)
COMPONENTS OF SOLAR SYSTEM	8	68.9(1.1)	69.7(1.7)	68.2(1.5)	72.4(1.4)	57.7(2.9)	62.7(2.3)
	12	69.3(1.1)	71.5(1.5)	67.4(1.4)	71.9(1.2)	58.2(3.2)	62.4(3.4)
COMMUNICATING ON THE MOON	8	58.7(1.3)	63.4(1.8)	53.9(1.5)	61.8(1.6)	45.9(2.6)	54.5(3.0)
	12	67.1(1.0)	74.3(1.5)	60.5(1.4)	68.5(1.3)	57.9(3.3)	66.1(3.9)
ANGLE OF REFLECTION	8	55.4(1.0)	62.0(1.6)	48.7(1.5)	59.4(1.2)	40.6(2.6)	45.9(2.0)
	12	62.5(1.1)	73.1(1.6)	52.9(1.5)	66.3(1.3)	46.1(2.6)	57.5(3.2)
EARTH'S CRUST: OLDEST LAYERS	8	47.7(1.3)	49.7(1.8)	45.6(1.5)	51.6(1.5)	31.9(3.2)	42.0(3.1)
	12	50.7(1.1)	49.3(1.6)	51.9(1.4)	53.1(1.2)	38.5(2.7)	50.9(3.9)
EARTH'S CRUST: CURVED LAYERS	8	41.3(1.3)	43.4(1.6)	39.1(1.9)	43.9(1.5)	31.3(3.1)	39.7(2.4)
	12	44.7(1.1)	51.3(1.4)	38.7(1.5)	47.1(1.2)	34.4(3.0)	38.3(2.4)
RAIN AND CORN GROWTH	8	48.5(1.2)	50.4(1.7)	46.6(1.5)	51.5(1.5)	41.4(2.6)	38.0(2.5)
	12	68.1(1.1)	69.6(1.2)	66.7(1.8)	70.9(1.4)	56.0(2.1)	60.0(3.5)
MEANING OF 20% CHANCE OF RAIN	8	19.9(1.0)	23.6(1.4)	16.2(1.2)	22.0(1.4)	12.4(1.3)	16.3(1.8)
	12	40.0(1.0)	48.0(1.4)	32.7(1.4)	44.6(1.2)	23.6(2.5)	26.2(2.4)
WATER EVAPORATION	12	37.3(1.4)	35.8(2.0)	38.7(1.7)	37.4(1.6)	35.5(2.8)	36.6(4.2)
REACTION RATES DURING EQUILIB	12	33.5(1.0)	37.4(1.7)	29.8(1.4)	33.5(1.2)	29.7(2.6)	32.3(2.9)
WHAT IS ACCURACY?	12	68.6(1.2)	64.5(1.4)	72.4(1.6)	71.2(1.4)	55.3(3.9)	58.9(4.7)
GRAPH:POPULATION/ADAPTATION	12	66.8(1.0)	70.0(1.5)	64.0(1.4)	68.5(1.1)	60.2(3.1)	64.9(2.7)
EINSTEIN'S E=MC2	12	78.8(0.9)	80.9(1.1)	76.9(1.1)	81.1(1.1)	70.8(2.6)	68.2(3.4)
INERTIA OF LEAD-FILLED BOX	12	57.4(0.9)	60.9(1.5)	54.3(1.1)	61.0(1.1)	44.0(2.5)	50.6(3.3)
TEST PREDICTIONS W/EXPERIMENT	12	64.5(1.1)	59.9(1.6)	68.7(1.3)	68.4(1.2)	50.4(3.3)	52.3(2.7)
HEAT GAS, INCREASE PRESSURE	12	67.2(0.9)	67.3(1.3)	67.1(1.4)	70.0(1.1)	55.1(3.2)	61.8(2.7)
EXP:EFFECT OF WT ON PENDULUM	12	48.6(1.4)	48.9(2.1)	48.3(1.5)	53.3(1.7)	30.3(2.8)	35.3(3.1)
RELATION OF PRESSURE/ALTITUDE	12	52.2(1.4)	53.6(1.7)	50.9(1.7)	53.7(1.5)	46.3(2.9)	49.9(3.7)
WHICH CAN BE TESTED?	12	54.5(1.3)	53.3(1.8)	55.6(1.6)	58.3(1.6)	41.1(2.9)	45.1(3.2)
GRAPH:GREATEST SOLUBILITY	12	72.6(0.9)	73.6(1.3)	71.7(1.4)	74.7(1.0)	63.5(2.9)	66.8(2.6)
GRAPH:GRAMS TO BE DISSOLVED	12	51.7(1.2)	54.3(1.9)	49.4(1.7)	55.1(1.5)	35.4(3.4)	43.1(2.7)
MASS INCREASE AS IRON RUSTS	12	18.2(0.9)	22.6(1.5)	14.1(1.0)	18.6(1.1)	14.2(2.6)	16.7(3.2)
EXP:TEST AIR POLLUTION	12	65.4(1.2)	65.0(1.4)	65.8(1.8)	69.3(1.4)	51.2(2.3)	54.5(3.6)

NAEP 1990 SCIENCE CROSS-SECTIONAL ASSESSMENT
Weighted Percentages of Students
Responding Correctly to Science Items

ITEM DESCRIPTION	GRADE	NATION	MALE	FEMALE	WHITE	BLACK	HISPANIC
DIAGRAM:NEW CRUST	12	29.2(1.2)	31.9(1.4)	26.7(1.5)	30.2(1.4)	27.8(2.3)	26.1(2.9)
DIAGRAM:SUBDUCTION	12	51.4(1.1)	56.8(1.8)	46.5(1.4)	54.6(1.2)	38.0(2.9)	45.6(2.6)
GRAPH:IMMUNE SYSTEM MEMORY	12	36.7(1.1)	41.4(1.7)	32.5(1.1)	39.1(1.4)	27.1(2.2)	30.8(3.0)
TABLE:PULLING OBJECTS	12	29.4(0.9)	35.8(1.5)	23.6(1.1)	31.9(1.2)	18.1(2.3)	23.3(2.6)
GRAPH:TEMP/O2 CONSUMED	12	43.0(1.3)	41.6(1.8)	44.2(1.4)	46.5(1.4)	30.9(3.0)	31.3(3.6)
GRAPH:02 CONSUMED AT 26°C	12	25.1(0.8)	24.7(1.6)	25.5(1.2)	25.4(0.9)	20.9(2.2)	24.8(2.9)
AIR MOVEMENT IN HIGH PRESSURE	12	40.5(1.2)	44.1(1.9)	37.2(1.4)	43.2(1.3)	29.8(2.3)	31.6(3.1)
EXPLOSION OF STAR	12	28.8(1.2)	34.7(1.8)	23.6(1.3)	31.5(1.5)	15.4(2.4)	26.1(3.6)
GENETIC PEDIGREE/SEX-LINKED	12	17.6(1.0)	14.7(1.2)	20.1(1.5)	18.2(1.2)	14.6(2.3)	14.2(3.3)
MAKE 1-MOLAR SOLUTION	12	22.6(1.0)	23.1(1.3)	22.2(1.3)	21.0(1.1)	28.1(3.5)	25.5(3.2)
WHY STRAWBERRIES APPEAR RED	12	37.6(1.4)	40.8(2.1)	34.8(1.8)	41.5(1.7)	21.5(2.0)	25.3(4.0)
COLORS IN WHITE LIGHT	12	59.4(1.2)	60.6(1.7)	58.4(1.4)	63.3(1.5)	44.9(3.0)	48.4(3.3)
TABLE:ELECTRICAL CONDUCTORS	12	70.3(1.1)	70.5(1.8)	70.1(1.1)	70.6(1.3)	66.7(2.2)	71.6(2.5)
FUNCTION OF PLANT STEM	12	59.9(1.1)	59.6(1.7)	60.1(1.6)	66.3(1.2)	34.5(3.0)	48.2(3.6)
POSITIONS OF STARS/PLANETS	12	57.6(1.0)	56.8(1.4)	58.4(1.5)	57.0(1.3)	56.8(2.8)	61.5(2.8)
INCREASE STRENGTH OF MAGNET	12	58.3(1.1)	59.8(1.4)	56.9(1.5)	59.8(1.2)	52.4(2.6)	55.5(3.3)
PROB OF M/F CHILDREN	12	50.8(1.2)	47.7(1.5)	53.6(1.8)	52.5(1.4)	42.3(2.8)	49.1(3.2)
EXP:DISSOLVE SELTZER	12	43.2(1.1)	42.5(1.3)	43.8(1.6)	47.8(1.2)	26.3(2.3)	32.8(3.0)
GRAVITY EFFECT ON SATELLITES	12	68.1(1.0)	68.5(1.6)	67.8(1.4)	69.0(1.2)	63.3(2.4)	67.1(2.9)
PHYLOGENETIC TREES	12	36.2(0.9)	37.7(1.5)	34.9(1.6)	37.3(1.0)	30.6(2.7)	36.5(2.2)
STEPS TO DEVELOP VACCINE	12	34.6(0.8)	33.7(1.1)	35.4(1.1)	34.9(1.0)	34.5(3.0)	29.4(3.2)
ANSWER QUESTION W/MEASUREMENT	12	51.2(1.3)	51.2(1.6)	51.3(1.5)	54.0(1.4)	37.9(2.8)	47.9(3.0)
1-LITER SAMPLES OF GASES	12	16.2(0.9)	17.1(1.3)	15.3(1.3)	16.0(1.1)	12.1(1.9)	20.5(2.4)
GRAPH:TEMP/ENERGY	12	25.2(1.0)	27.1(1.6)	23.6(1.2)	25.0(1.3)	21.9(1.9)	24.0(2.9)
WAYS TO MEASURE REACTION RATE	12	25.4(1.0)	26.3(1.6)	24.6(1.1)	25.7(1.2)	22.7(1.9)	24.4(3.1)
RATIO OF LIQUID/GAS DENSITY	12	8.9(0.6)	6.6(0.8)	10.9(1.2)	8.2(0.7)	10.8(2.0)	10.0(2.3)
SPEED OF SOUND-EXPLORERS	12	25.2(1.0)	25.1(1.3)	25.3(1.5)	24.1(0.9)	26.4(2.6)	29.2(2.7)

NAEP 1990 SCIENCE CROSS-SECTIONAL ASSESSMENT
Weighted Percentages of Students
Responding Correctly to Science Items

ITEM DESCRIPTION	GRADE	NATION	MALE	FEMALE	WHITE	BLACK	HISPANIC
GENETIC ENGINEERING	12	60.7(1.7)	56.0(2.4)	64.8(1.8)	63.3(1.9)	44.4(3.8)	55.7(4.5)
NEW ELEMENT:REPEAT EXP	12	46.5(1.5)	47.3(2.2)	45.7(1.7)	47.7(1.6)	36.6(3.1)	49.7(5.8)
TABLE:CAUSES OF DEATH	12	57.7(1.4)	56.7(1.8)	58.6(2.3)	61.6(1.7)	42.2(3.6)	47.4(5.3)
CAPACITOR CHARGE AND TIME	12	15.1(1.0)	18.0(1.5)	12.0(1.2)	15.6(1.2)	10.0(2.0)	15.8(4.4)
ALTITUDE PROFILE	12	16.1(1.2)	21.3(1.8)	10.7(1.1)	17.2(1.3)	5.2(2.1)	10.7(2.4)
HALF-LIFE GRAPH	12	23.3(1.4)	29.2(2.0)	16.8(1.6)	24.8(1.4)	5.1(1.9)	14.7(4.2)
FOSSILS ON 2 CONTINENTS	12	80.7(0.9)	82.3(1.2)	79.2(1.3)	83.7(1.0)	67.4(3.1)	73.4(2.8)
EXP:EFFECT OF VITAMIN K	12	51.6(1.2)	47.0(1.6)	55.8(1.3)	55.7(1.3)	32.3(2.6)	46.3(2.8)
MODEL OF ATOMS' BEHAVIOR	12	55.9(1.1)	53.2(1.6)	58.4(1.4)	61.2(1.3)	37.6(2.7)	39.2(2.7)
DIAGRAM:STOMACH	12	81.1(1.0)	83.9(1.5)	78.5(1.3)	85.1(0.9)	69.0(2.3)	67.0(3.3)
DIAGRAM:SOURCE OF INSULIN	12	58.4(1.1)	59.8(1.9)	57.1(1.6)	60.5(1.4)	50.5(3.3)	53.0(3.7)
SPECIFIC HEAT OF H2O/OIL	12	26.7(1.0)	27.7(1.3)	25.7(1.4)	26.6(1.1)	26.9(2.6)	24.9(3.2)
INCREASE GREENHOUSE EFFECT	12	61.2(1.3)	65.5(1.6)	57.2(1.6)	65.8(1.4)	42.0(2.8)	50.1(3.2)
GRAPH:VELOCITY OF 3 OBJECTS	12	34.2(1.5)	37.1(2.2)	31.5(1.7)	35.2(1.7)	29.0(2.9)	30.6(3.4)
GRAPH:COOLING OF 2 LIQUIDS	12	37.8(1.2)	39.7(1.7)	36.0(1.5)	40.7(1.5)	24.7(2.4)	30.4(2.8)
SHADOWS-NORTH	12	20.8(0.8)	21.2(1.1)	20.4(1.2)	22.1(1.0)	17.4(2.3)	17.7(2.4)
SHADOWS-LABEL	12	28.7(1.0)	30.7(1.2)	26.9(1.4)	31.9(1.4)	13.0(2.0)	20.0(2.5)
SHADOWS-LENGTH	12	36.5(1.3)	42.4(2.0)	31.0(1.5)	41.1(1.5)	15.4(2.7)	27.8(3.8)
NUCLEAR POWER	12	54.6(1.7)	59.6(2.1)	49.8(1.9)	58.4(1.7)	36.2(4.3)	36.6(4.7)
GRAPH:VELOCITY/TIME	12	16.5(0.9)	20.6(1.4)	13.0(1.1)	15.9(1.1)	15.9(1.9)	19.4(2.8)
CAUSE OF SEASONS	12	28.5(1.2)	33.5(1.9)	24.1(1.5)	30.1(1.3)	19.9(2.9)	22.4(3.3)
POISONS IN FOOD CHAINS	12	76.6(1.2)	76.9(1.6)	76.4(1.5)	79.2(1.5)	64.7(3.1)	70.3(3.3)
WHY PUBLISH? SHARE FINDINGS	12	83.6(1.0)	80.9(1.8)	86.2(1.1)	85.2(1.3)	77.8(1.8)	78.0(3.7)
WHY PUBLISH? CHECK FINDINGS	12	77.6(1.0)	76.8(1.4)	78.2(1.3)	78.5(1.2)	72.2(2.7)	75.8(2.6)
WHY PUBLISH? ADD TO KNOWLEDGE	12	84.6(0.9)	84.4(1.3)	84.7(1.4)	87.0(1.2)	73.9(2.4)	82.6(2.6)
OCEAN CURRENTS AND CLIMATE	12	32.0(1.2)	36.2(1.5)	28.2(1.5)	33.9(1.3)	19.2(2.2)	26.5(3.8)
LIGHT BULBS IN SERIES	12	26.1(1.0)	32.1(1.5)	20.7(1.3)	28.5(1.1)	14.4(2.0)	21.0(2.9)

NAEP 1990 SCIENCE CROSS-SECTIONAL ASSESSMENT
Weighted Percentages of Students
Responding Correctly to Science Items

ITEM DESCRIPTION	GRADE	NATION	MALE	FEMALE	WHITE	BLACK	HISPANIC
INTERPRET A CHEMICAL FORMULA	12	56.8(1.1)	56.8(1.6)	56.9(1.6)	59.2(1.3)	48.5(2.4)	50.4(4.6)
ANALYZING CAUSES OF DISEASE	12	49.1(1.1)	47.5(1.4)	50.5(1.6)	51.5(1.2)	38.2(2.9)	41.9(4.4)
RATIO OF OXYGEN/COPPER	12	49.4(1.4)	50.1(1.8)	48.8(1.9)	51.7(1.6)	37.7(3.4)	44.1(2.9)
PLANT EXPERIMENT: CONTROL	12	78.9(1.0)	74.5(1.3)	82.8(1.1)	81.8(1.3)	66.7(2.6)	72.0(2.5)
BALANCING A CHEMICAL EQUATION	12	51.0(1.7)	48.9(2.4)	52.8(1.8)	54.2(2.2)	36.5(2.7)	39.1(3.5)

Acknowledgments

This report is the culmination of efforts by many individuals who contributed their considerable knowledge, experience, creativity, and energy to the development, administration, scoring, analysis, and reporting of the 1990 NAEP science assessment. Most importantly, NAEP is grateful to the students and school staff who made the assessment possible.

The 1990 NAEP science assessment was funded through the National Center for Education Statistics, in the Office of Educational Research and Improvement of the U.S. Department of Education. Emerson Elliott, NCES Acting Commissioner, provided consistent support and guidance, and his staff — particularly Gary Phillips, Eugene Owen, Steven Gorman, and Carol Sue Fromboluti — worked closely and collegially with ETS.

Under the NAEP contract to ETS, Archie Lapointe served as the project director and Ina Mullis as the deputy director. The science assessment development activities were coordinated by Walter MacDonald. The statistical and psychometric activities were led by Nancy Allen with direction from Eugene Johnson and Rebecca Zwick, assistance from Angela Grima and Joling Liang, and consultation from Kentaro Yamamoto. John Barone managed the data analysis activities, and the analyses reported herein were conducted by Steven Isham, with assistance from David Freund, Edward Kulick, and Phillip Leung. Jules Goodison directed the operational aspects of the assessment. Westat, Inc., under the supervision of Renee Slobasky, Keith Rust, and Nancy Caldwell, coordinated and performed sampling and data collection activities. The printing, distribution, and processing of the materials were the responsibility of National Computer Systems, under the direction of Lynn Zaback and John O'Neill.

Lee Jones, Ina Mullis, Senta Raizen, Iris Weiss, and Elizabeth Weston wrote the text for the report. Many thanks are due to the numerous reviewers who suggested improvements to successive drafts, especially Nancy Allen, Mary Foertsch, Steven Isham, Eugene Johnson, Stephen Koffler, and John Olson. Margaret Mate, Sharon Davis-Johnson, and Alice Kass provided the excellent word-processing skills essential to the project. Kent Ashworth, Rebekkah Melchor Logan, and the ETS Publications Division coordinated the final production of this report, which was designed by Rivermead Studio.

To order additional copies of
THE 1990 SCIENCE REPORT CARD
please use the order form below.

Superintendent of Documents **Publication** Order Form

Order Processing Code:
*6242

☐ **YES,** please send me the following publication:

_____ copies of **THE 1990 SCIENCE REPORT CARD**, S/N 065-000-00490-9 at $11 each.

The total cost of my order is $_____. International customers please add 25%. Price includes regular domestic postage and handling and is subject to change.

Charge your order.
It's Easy! MasterCard VISA
To fax your orders (202) 512–2250

_____
(Company or Personal Name)   (Please type or print)

_____
(Additional address/attention line)

_____
(Street address)

_____
(City, State, ZIP Code)

_____
(Daytime phone including area code)

_____
(Purchase Order No.)
                                    YES NO
May we make your name/address available to other mailers? ☐   ☐

Please Choose Method of Payment:

☐ Check Payable to the Superintendent of Documents

☐ GPO Deposit Account ☐☐☐☐☐☐☐–☐

☐ VISA or MasterCard Account

☐☐☐☐☐☐☐☐☐☐☐☐☐☐☐☐☐☐☐☐

☐☐☐☐ (Credit card expiration date)   *Thank you for your order!*

_____
(Authorizing Signature)   3/92

Mail To: Superintendent of Documents
          P.O. Box 371954, Pittsburgh, PA 15250–7954

or order from your nearest Government Bookstore

U.S. Government Bookstores are located in the following cities: Atlanta, Denver, New York, Birmingham, Ala., Detroit, Philadelphia, Boston, Houston, Pittsburgh, Chicago, Jacksonville, Fla., Portland, Ore., Cleveland, Kansas City, Mo., Pueblo, Colo., Columbus, Laurel, Md., San Francisco, Dallas, Los Angeles, Seattle, Milwaukee and Washington, D.C. **(See your yellow pages.)**

Photocopies of this order form are acceptable.